Introduction to
Control Engineering

Introduction to Control Engineering

Michael Dickinson

Elektor International Media
www.elektor.com

British Library Cataloguing in Publication Data
A catalogue record for this book is available from the British Library

ISBN 978-0-905705-99-6

Prepress production: Eric A.J. Bogers, Aschendorf (DE)
Cover Design: Etcetera, Aachen (DE)
First published in the United Kingdom 2011
Printed in the Netherlands by Wilco, Amersfoort

109036-UK

Table of Contents

About the author

Michael Dickinson graduated in Control Engineering from Sheffield Hallam University in 1981. He worked in local industry as an electronic and software design engineer for several years, gaining particular experience in analogue and digital electronics, microprocessor interfacing and embedded software for plant control applications.

He returned to Sheffield Hallam University as a lecturer in Control Engineering, teaching electronics, software and control theory. During this time, he was specifically responsible for admissions to the Degree and HND programmes in electronics and control engineering.

Whilst lecturing, he gained his PhD by part-time study at the University of Sheffield, with research into sensors for robotic applications.

Since 1992, he has been involved running a small electronic and software engineering company providing control solutions to metal-forming and process industries, with particular experience in electro-hydraulic control systems.

He is a council member and is at the time of writing, chairman of the International Institute of Metal-forming.

Michael is married with three children and spends his spare time fell-walking.

About this book

This book is aimed at practising engineers, students and hobbyists. It is intended as a source of reference for hardware and software associated with instrumentation and control engineering. Examples are presented from a range of industries and applications.

Control engineering as a discipline is not widely taught, so engineers from different backgrounds are often required to determine an appropriate solution from an unfamiliar area of experience. The book attempts to provide an introduction to the principles of control engineering and to provide tools to enable such solutions to be realised. The book is not intended as an exhaustive text on control theory, in fact much detail has been left out in the interest of application and industrial practice. Hopefully, this book serves as a reference, by illustration of the basic principles, supported by examples of current methodology, practical hardware and software.

Throughout the book, circuit diagrams and software listings are described, typical of many measurement and control applications. The hardware and software designs may be used as a basis for application by the reader.

There is an emphasis on software throughout the text, with examples of PIC, PAC and PC programming. Development software for all such devices is relatively cheap, and the examples presented are to encourage the reader to experiment with the technologies. Code is shown in C, assembler or structured English, from which readers will be able to repeat the techniques on most computing platforms. Example systems are presented early in the book, with analysis, followed by simulation, control solutions and programmes. Effects of parameter variation may be observed in the simulations. Practical electronic circuits are described for common processing applications, with analysis of operation and design.

The building blocks and theory presented are brought together in the final chapter which presents a simulation of a complete control scheme with three term control, illustrating how such a system may be configured.

Software sources

Software examples in the book are written in PIC assembler, C++ or C#. Readers are invited to reproduce and modify the examples for their own purposes. Software tools are available as follows:

⟾   Visual C++ and Visual C# are part of the Microsoft "Visual Studio" suite, and are available as free downloads from their web site

http://www.microsoft.com/express/download

⟾   the PIC assembly language programmes presented are written for Microchip family of devices. For further detail see

http://www.microchip.com

⟾   the MPLAB IDE is a complete PC based development environment, with editor, assembler, linker and simulator. Programmes may be written and tested completely within the IDE. To transfer programmes to a processor, the "PICSTART" programmer is recommended. A C compiler is also available.

Refer to "distributors" for details of local retailers. Software tools, support and hardware for the Microchip family are generally widely available through professional retailers, user groups and technical publications.

Trademarks, names and copyright of the above suppliers are recognised.

1
Introduction

What is Control Engineering?

Control Engineering is a relatively new discipline which has grown alongside technological development with the need for greater process information and control. As we have sought to mass produce and develop further our manufacturing skills, there has been a requirement to measure output and to control performance of such processes much more effectively. In recent years, the required tools have also developed significantly, enabling the control engineer to model, analyse and create sophisticated control systems, operating not only in manufacturing industry, but also in other spheres where measurement, modelling and control have proved effective (eg financial modelling, biological applications, multivariable systems).

Control engineering is a discipline in its own right in that there is an underlying base of "control theory", and is unique in that it draws heavily upon other subject areas. Control theory relies upon elements of mathematics for analytical tools and modelling techniques. Typically, a practical solution requires skills in electrical and electronic engineering, as well as computer hardware and software engineering, often for a mechanical problem. The control engineer therefore requires knowledge of all of these subject areas to perform effectively.

The essence of Control Engineering is to provide measurement and control of a particular variable (or variables) of interest. In continuous process industries, this typically involves control of "fluid" variables such as temperature, pressure, flow and level (eg chemical processing, oil and gas, food and beverages, pharmaceuticals). In the automation industries, control of "mechanical" variables, such as position, speed and acceleration are important (eg robotics, guided vehicles, CNC machines).

Before any variable may be controlled, it must be measured. Instrumentation has developed alongside control engineering since knowledge of the nature and range of the variable is essential to successful control.

Open and Closed Loop Control

By way of a trivial example to illustrate a point, consider the driver of a car, having an accelerator pedal to adjust the speed of a vehicle, as shown in figure 1.1. By depression of the accelerator, more fuel is allowed into the engine, which in turn produces more effort to the wheels and so the vehicle travels at a greater speed.

Such a system is effective in that control is available, but is subject to outside influence or disturbances. For example, as the vehicle approaches a hill, the speed would fall unless correction was made by further depression of the accelerator. Such a system is referred to as an "open loop" system.

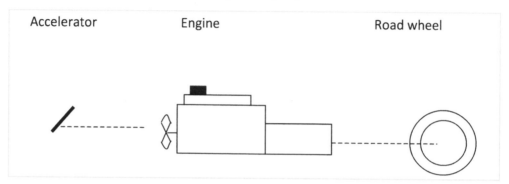

Figure 1.1   Open loop system, vehicle speed control

The concept of feedback has been developed since the 1920's and forms the basis of control theory. Measurement of the output of the system is essential in that comparison can be made between a desired (input) value and an actual (output) value. By subtraction of the measured output from the input, the difference is determined, called the "error". The controller can then be configured such that the error is used to drive the output in such a direction as to reduce that error to zero.

Such feedback is termed "negative feedback", since it subtracts from the input demand.

Consider again the vehicle, but now equipped with a speedometer, as shown in figure 1.2, in the form of a block diagram. The driver is now presented with a numerical value for the vehicle speed, displayed in an appropriate measurement unit (eg miles per hour, kilometres per hour etc), and so is able to regulate the accelerator depression to maintain a desired speed.

In this manner, the loop is closed, giving the driver some feedback by means of the speed measurement. The driver has become the system controller, by making a comparison between the measurement and the desired value, and making an appropriate correction to regulate the vehicle speed.

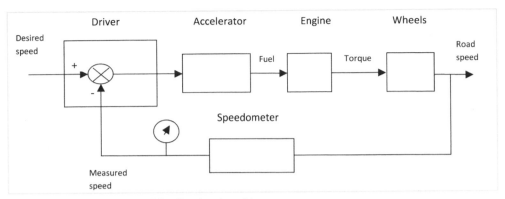

Figure 1.2   Application of feedback, closed loop

We have established then, an excellent example of the control engineering problem. There are three significant parts to the simple system:

⟹   the accelerator, engine and wheels, which make up the **"forward path"**, ie an input stimulus producing a change in the system output;

⟹   the speedometer, which is the **"feedback path"**, providing a measurement of the output;

⟹   the driver, shown here as a subtraction operation, which determines the difference between a desired value and the actual value, and makes an adjustment to suit, ie the **"system controller"**.

Any control system can be represented in a similar format and figure 1.3 shows the general case. There must always be a comparison between the desired value (set-point, reference, input) and the actual value (system output, controlled variable, measured value) to produce a system "error", followed by a correcting control action. The devices used depend upon the application, but the controller will generally be electronic or software.

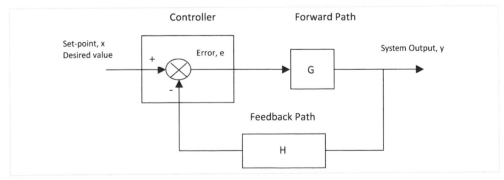

Figure 1.3   General closed loop system

Considering the forward path, we have,

$$y = Ge$$

(ie the original open loop system). Considering the feedback path, we can also say,

$$e = x - Hy$$

Substituting for the error, e, we have

$$y = G(x - Hy)$$

By rearrangement we determine the overall relationship between input x, and output, y,

$$y = Gx - GHy$$

So

$$y(1 + GH) = Gx$$

And

$$y = x \cdot \frac{G}{1 + GH}$$

This equation is called the system "transfer function", where the output, y, is a result of input, x, the system forward path parameters, G, and the feedback path parameters, H.

The function GH is referred to as the "loop gain" since it describes the system behaviour from input stimulus x, through to the returned feedback signal y, the output from the feedback device.

GH therefore includes all system parameters and is itself representative of system performance. In particular, considering the above closed loop transfer function, if GH were to tend towards -1, then the closed loop system would have infinite gain and become unstable, effectively sustaining an output for zero input.

The term $(1 + GH)$ is called the "characteristic equation" since it contains reference to all components within the system.

Time Response

Consider another simple but more realistic example to highlight other aspects of control engineering. Figure 1.4 shows a furnace where it is desired to control the temperature, in order to perform heating or a treatment process on items inside. The furnace is electrically heated and has a closed loop controller. The operator would have some means of entering a set-point temperature, and the actual temperature is measured with a suitable sensor, providing feedback and display.

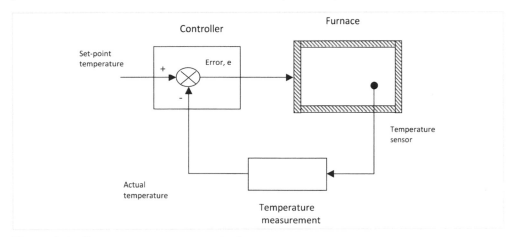

Figure 1.4   Furnace temperature control

At the point of switch on, the furnace temperature would be below the set-point, so there would be a significant temperature error and the heater would be fully on. As the temperature inside the furnace increased, we would expect to see the feedback signal increase, so the error, and hence the power to the heater, would reduce. Eventually the steady state would be reached when the furnace temperature has stabilised, the heater providing power into the furnace to match any losses and the temperature remains constant, hopefully close to the set-point.

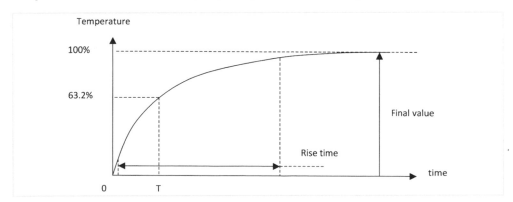

Figure 1.5   Furnace temperature time response

The furnace behaviour can be visualised as shown in figure 1.5. This is called the "time response" or "transient response" of the furnace, since it shows the behaviour of the controlled variable (ie temperature) against time as a result of a change in input. There are several features of the time response, in which control engineers are interested,

Rise time	the time taken for the output variable to change from 10% of the final value to 90% of the final value. It is therefore a measure of the speed of response of the system to a change in the input
Time constant	the time taken for the output to reach 63.2% of the final value, shown as "T" in the figure (The significance of the 63.2% will be discussed in a later chapter)
Steady state value	the final output value reached (ie when the output is steady)

We shall observe in a later chapter that the time constant is dependent upon the component parts of the system and their physical parameters (in this case the heater power, sensor characteristics and furnace characteristics etc).

The example shows a gradual increase in temperature to the steady state value. The response may have been as shown in figure 1.6, where the output overshoots the set-point value, causing the heater to be turned off. As the furnace then cools, the temperature would fall below the set-point, causing the heater to increase the temperature again. This would be repeated until the steady state is achieved.

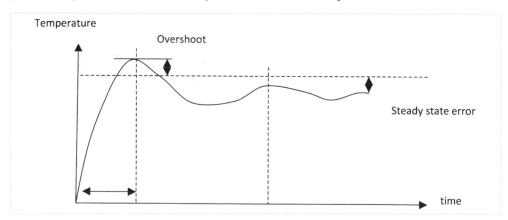

Figure 1.6 *Furnace temperature time response*

In this case, the features of interest are

Overshoot (%)	the amount (%) by which the output overshoots (exceeds) the final value
First overshoot time	the time taken to reach the first overshoot is a measure of response time
Settling Time	the time taken for the output to reach a stable state (normally defined as having settled to within 5% of the final value)
Settling Frequency	the rate at which the oscillations occur, ie a measure of the response of the system
Steady State Error	the difference between the set-point and the final value

For most applications it is the time response which is of greatest interest, particularly since we wish the output to follow an input request as closely as possible. Control of the system is in the interest of minimising the steady state error and minimising any overshoot whilst making the rise time or settling time as short as possible.

Frequency Response

While the time response of a system delivers sufficient information for design and operation of a control system, there are other aspects of which we must be aware. Considering again the block diagram in figure 1.3 and the transfer function for the closed loop system, we noted that the "loop gain" is *GH*, and if *GH* were to equal –1, the denominator of the transfer function would be zero, and our system would exhibit infinite gain.

It is therefore essential that we consider the phase of the feedback signal, and ensure that the feedback is always negative within the scope of operation of the system. This leads us to study the "frequency response" of the system, to observe how it responds at different frequencies, and to check that the loop gain does not approach –1 at any frequency. (A gain of –1 is a gain of 1 with a phase shift of 180°).

The frequency response of a system is represented graphically, showing gain and phase change over a range of frequencies, as depicted in figure 1.7. Note that a complete description of frequency response has two parts,

➠ a measure of gain against frequency

➠ a measure of phase against frequency

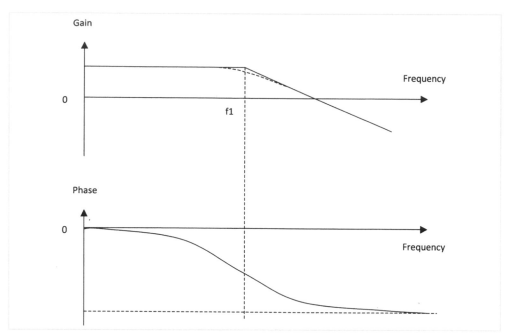

Figure 1.7 *System frequency response*

Figure 1.7 depicts the frequency response of a typical system using straight line ap-proximation for the purpose of explanation. Practical systems will exhibit similar characteristics. The frequency response has the following salient features:

⟹ gain will be constant at low frequencies, as the system is able to respond ac-curately to changes in input stimulus. As the rate of change of input stimulus increases (ie frequency) the physical system is unable to respond so quickly, so the system gain is reduced (the output cannot change by the magnitude the input signal demands, since it is restricted by the physical and practical constraints of its component parts);

⟹ gain will fall off at a constant rate as frequency increases. The rate of de-crease depends upon the component parts of the system;

⟹ phase is typically negative for practical systems, ie a phase lag. The output variable cannot respond instantly, so will always be "lagging behind" the in-put stimulus. As frequency increases, the phase shift tends towards a maxi-mum;

⟹ the "transition frequency" shown as f1 above is significant, being the point at which the gain has fallen to 0.707 of its low frequency value and the phase shift is half the high frequency shift. This frequency point has direct relation to the "time constant" of the system (in the time response above).

We shall see in a later chapter the relationship between the time response and the frequency response of a system and how they are related to the physical components.

Stability

So far, we have considered the use of feedback to produce an error signal, that error signal being of polarity to drive the forward path in such a direction as to reduce the error. This feedback is termed "negative feedback", since it subtracts from the input demand.

We have already considered a situation where the loop gain GH tends towards -1. In practical terms, we would have the situation where the feedback is positive, hence adding to the system input to produce a greater output. In this situation, no input is required to produce an output, so the system becomes unstable and oscillates. We shall consider stability further and realise the significance of the time and frequency response analysis in later chapters.

Summary

This chapter has presented simple examples to illustrate the application of feedback within control systems, and has defined open loop and closed loop systems. It has introduced and defined terms used in control engineering to describe system performance. Time response, frequency response and stability have been considered.

2
System Modelling

An essential part of control engineering is to understand the process to be controlled and to be able to recognise familiar elements within that system. This is achieved easily by creation of an appropriate system model, which will represent all the component parts of a system, indicate all the physical variables present and then allow further analysis.

There are various modelling tools and techniques available to the control engineer, the method chosen usually being by personal preference or for expedience. In particular, we shall consider the most common methods of modelling, using mathematical description by transfer functions in the Laplace domain aided by suitable block diagrams. These techniques will help to form an understanding of commonly encountered system elements and will lay a foundation towards easy system simulation and performance analysis in later chapters.

This chapter shows how a control system may be broken down into component parts, presented in block diagram form and then represented mathematically. The end result is the "transfer function", which relates the output of the system to the input. The modelling techniques are shown in the following examples.

Example 1 – A simple RC network

In this example, a voltage V_{in}, is applied to a simple RC network, with resistance R, and capacitance C, as shown in figure 2.1.

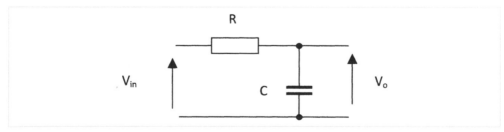

Figure 2.1 *RC Network*

To begin the modelling process, we write the basic equations for the physical components, usually expressed as functions of time (t), and for many systems are differential equations.

We have,

$$V_{in} = V_o + iR$$

But

$$i = C \cdot \frac{dV_o}{dt}$$

So

$$V_{in} = V_o + RC \cdot \frac{dV_o}{dt}$$

At this point we reach the difficulty of separating "V_o" in the equation, since it is expressed as a differential with respect to time. Using one of the control engineer's most useful tools, the Laplace transform, we can rewrite the expression in the "s domain":

$$V_{in}(s) = V_o(s) + sRC \cdot V_o(s)$$

Hence

$$V_{in}(s) = V_o(s) \cdot (1 + sRC)$$

And finally we have the transfer function, expressed in the Laplace domain,

$$V_o = V_{in} \cdot \frac{1}{1 + sRC}$$

Or

$$\frac{V_o}{V_{in}} = \frac{K}{1 + sT} \quad \text{where } K = 1 \text{ and } T = RC$$

This is purposely presented in standard form, such that K is referred to as the "forward path gain", representing the transfer ratio (gain) in steady state conditions (ie in this example, in the steady state, $V_o = 1 \cdot V_{in}$, a gain of 1, when the capacitor has charged to the input voltage).

EXAMPLE 1 – A SIMPLE RC NETWORK

The "s" indicates the time-changing behaviour of the system, brought about by the differential properties. T is referred to as the system "time constant", being descriptive of that time varying behaviour, and as expected, depends upon the physical properties of the system, in this case the value of resistance and capacitance, R and C. In practical terms, larger values of R and C would increase the time constant, since a large resistance would limit the charging current and a larger capacitance would take longer to charge.

So now we have the transfer function for the RC network, it is possible to use it to determine the output from the system when particular inputs are applied. We can then revert back to the time domain (expressing the output in terms of time, t) to visualise the output voltage characteristic.

Suppose we were to apply the input voltage V_{in} by switch closure, so V_{in} changes instantaneously from zero to a given voltage. We refer to this as a "step change", and there is a convenient model for it in the Laplace domain, by expressing the step change as

$$\frac{V_{in}}{s}$$

The output V_o (expressed in the Laplace domain) would therefore be

$$V_o(s) = \frac{V_{in}}{s} \cdot \frac{1}{1 + sRC} = \frac{V_{in}}{s \cdot (1 + sRC)}$$

At this juncture, we refer to the Laplace transform tables, and determine the appropriate time domain equivalent of the resulting expression. In this case, taking inverse Laplace transforms, we have

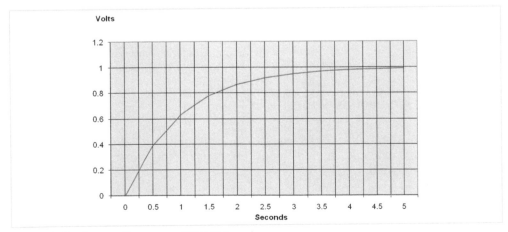

Figure 2.2 *Output Response of RC Network*

$$V_{\mathrm{o}}(t) = V_{\mathrm{in}}(t) \cdot \left(1 - e^{-\frac{t}{RC}} \right)$$

By substitution of the values for R and C, the expression can be solved. Figure 2.2 shows the output voltage V_{o}, as a result of the step input V_{in}, of 1 Volt.

Aside – Laplace Transforms

The Laplace transform technique is particularly important and is a major tool in control system analysis.

There are many undergraduate texts available which present a sound mathematical basis and it is not intended to expand on the technique here. The reader is encouraged to view alternative reference texts, given that it is a mathematical tool for handling and solving differential equations, and is used in other spheres outside of control engineering.

The technique provides a simple, convenient method for solution of differential equations using standard types and table look-up.

For the control engineer, it is more important to recognise physical components and properties within a system and be able to express the relationships between those components and associated variables. The Laplace transform is then used merely as a tool for convenient expression and solution.

Essentially, a control engineer would take the following steps,

1   Represent the physical system in differential equation form

2   Convert into the Laplace domain (s)

3   Manipulate the expression using standard algebraic rules to present the system in a standard form

4   Convert the resulting expression back into the time domain (t)

5   Calculate accordingly to determine the output as a function of time

Example 2 – A dc servomotor

In a similar way, the transfer function and response of a dc servomotor may be determined. In this example, an additional tool is used (the block diagram) to help visualise the component parts.

Consider a dc servomotor, having a permanent magnet field. The motor drives a load comprising a frictional component and an inertial component, as represented in figure 2.3:

EXAMPLE 2 – A DC SERVOMOTOR

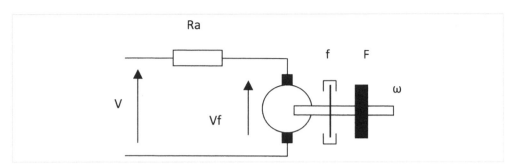

Figure 2.3 *DC Servo-motor*

To model the motor, we begin with the basic physical relationships as in the previous example. Beginning at the system input and working towards the output, we write a relation for each component part. We have,

Motor armature current

$$i_a = V - \frac{V_f}{R_a}$$

V_f is the back emf proportional to speed, hence

$$V_f = K_\omega \omega$$

Torque produced is proportional to armature current, hence

$$Torque = K_t i_a$$

For the load, the torque is applied to a shaft having friction and inertia, hence from our basic physical relationships

$$Torque(t) = J\frac{d\omega}{dt} + f\omega$$

We now have enough to create our model of the motor, and show it in block diagram form. Note that each component is represented as a block, while the interconnecting lines represent the physical variables at input and output. The transfer function of each block is marked inside the block, relating the output variable to the input variable, the function within the block comprising the physical parameters of the component represented. Figure 2.4 shows the block diagram for the motor.

The first block is the armature, which we assume has resistance R_a, and negligible inductance. The block output is the armature current which will flow as a result of

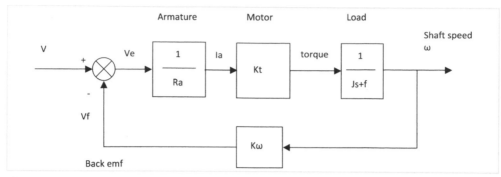

Figure 2.4 *DC Servomotor block diagram*

the effective armature voltage (applied voltage V minus the generated back emf). The motor itself produces torque as a result of the armature current. The motor is modelled by a torque constant K_t, representing the "motor effect" of the force produced by current flowing through a conductor in a magnetic field. The motor shaft has friction (in the bearings and any applied load) and it has inertia (stored energy, flywheel effect). The load is therefore represented as a combination of friction and inertia, from which the shaft speed is the system output as a result of the applied torque.

Note that in the figure the load has been represented directly in the Laplace domain,

$$Torque(s) = Js\omega + f\omega$$

From which

$$\omega(s) = \frac{Torque}{Js + f}$$

As the motor shaft rotates, a "back emf" is generated, which opposes the applied armature voltage. This is shown in the feedback block as $K\omega$, a constant relating the generated voltage to the shaft speed. The subtraction represents the negative effect of the back emf on the applied armature voltage, V.

Having produced the block diagram, we can proceed to determine the system overall transfer function, relating motor speed to applied voltage.

From the forward path, we can write

$$\omega(s) = V_e \cdot \frac{K_t}{R_a(Js + f)}$$

EXAMPLE 2 – A DC SERVOMOTOR

At the summing junction,

$$V_e = V - K_\omega \omega$$

So we can substitute for V_e, such that

$$\omega(s) = V \cdot \frac{K_t}{R_a(Js + f)} - \frac{\omega K_\omega K_t}{R_a(Js + f)}$$

We wish to obtain a relationship between ω and V, so after re-arrangement, we have again a standard first-order transfer function,

$$\omega(s) = V(s) \cdot \frac{K}{1 + sT}$$

where

$$K = \frac{K_t}{f R_a + K_\omega K_t} \quad \text{and} \quad T = \frac{J R_a}{f R_a + K_\omega K_t}$$

As expected, in practical terms,

➠ the forward path gain is influenced by the torque constant, armature resistance and frictional load (note their respective position on the numerator or denominator and consider the effect on the output speed);

➠ the time constant is influenced by the inertia and the armature resistance, an increase in either of which would delay the response of the motor as it accelerates up to speed.

Similarly, we can apply a step change to the applied voltage and observe the output speed of the motor. For a step input voltage, V,

$$\omega(s) = V(s) \cdot \frac{K}{1 + sT}$$

So

$$\omega(t) = V(t) \cdot \left(1 - e^{-\frac{t}{T}}\right)$$

To complete the model, we consider a practical motor, for which

Rated armature voltage	24	volts
Armature resistance	0.6	ohm
Torque constant	0.08	Nm / amp
emf constant	8.6	Volt / 1000 rpm

driving a load, for which

| Load inertia, J | 600 | Kgcm^2 |
| Load friction, f | 0.2 | Nm |

Note:

When taking numerical data from manufacturer information for modelling purposes, it is essential to ensure that units are consistent and correct. In the above, the emf constant is expressed in "volts per 1000 rpm" and inertia is expressed in Kgcm^2, being the units in which the manufacturer has chosen for expression. The values should be converted to standard MKS units for equation solution.

For the motor,

$$\omega(s) = V(s) \cdot \frac{0.5}{1 + s \cdot 0.22}$$

So

$$\omega(t) = V(t) \cdot 0.5 \cdot \left(1 - e^{-\frac{t}{0.22}}\right)$$

Assuming a 24 Volt dc supply applied to the motor as a step change, the function is solved and shown in figure 2.5.

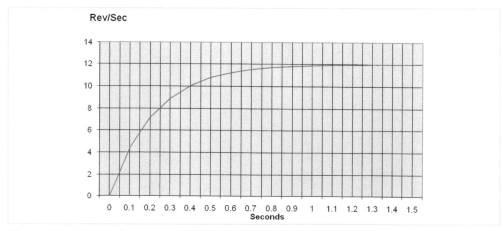

Figure 2.5 *Output Response of DC Servomotor*

Closing the Loop

The motor modelled above is a simple open loop system. When operated at the rated armature voltage, the output shaft speed will vary dependent upon the applied load. Note in particular that the load friction is significant in the forward path gain – increasing friction results in a lower shaft speed, as would be expected in a practical situation. In most applications, it is required to maintain a constant shaft speed under varying load conditions, and is useful to be able to set a desired speed within the range of the motor rating (ie a variable speed drive). Consider then the application of feedback from a tacho-generator to close the loop using a simple feedback controller. Figure 2.6 shows the closed loop system, where K_f is the feedback coefficient for the tacho-generator expressed in volts / rev per sec.

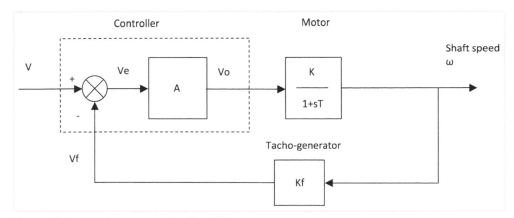

Figure 2.6   DC Servomotor in closed loop

The motor is modelled as a first order system as derived above, and is shown as the forward path of the system along with the drive amplifier. The tacho-generator is the feedback, hence for the closed loop, we have

$$\omega = V_e \cdot \frac{AK}{1 + sT}$$

and

$$V_e = V - K_f \omega$$

So the overall transfer function for the closed loop system is obtained after rearrangement, and may still be expressed as a standard first-order transfer function,

$$\omega(s) = V(s) \cdot \frac{G}{1 + sT}$$

But note that in the closed loop application, we have a different forward path gain

$$G = \frac{AK}{1 + AKK_{\mathrm{f}}}$$

Where K is the original servomotor gain constant as derived above for the open loop motor.

We also have a much reduced time constant (the same time constant as in the open loop system reduced by a function of amplifier gain and feedback coefficient),

$$T = \frac{\dfrac{JR_{\mathrm{a}}}{f R_{\mathrm{a}} + K_{\omega} K_{\mathrm{t}}}}{1 + AKK_{\mathrm{f}}}$$

Note that by closing the loop, there are significant changes to the system performance:

⇒   the effective time constant is reduced significantly, since an increased voltage would be applied to the armature throughout the acceleration period, rather than the (effectively reducing) armature voltage in the open loop application (although in practice this would be limited by amplifier voltage "headroom" and availability of drive current from the amplifier);

⇒   in the steady state, the error is significantly lower, reducing with increasing amplifier gain.

To complete the model of the closed loop system, we retain the motor parameters as above, and consider a practical application. In system design, we would prefer a standard input voltage range, 0 – 10 V for example, to produce from zero to full motor speed. For the tacho-generator, a standard type might produce 0 – 10 V for 0 – 2000 rpm. Converting to standard units for solution in the time domain, we have

V_{in}	10	volts
K_{f}	0.3	volts per rev/sec

The amplifier gain A, is variable, and we shall use a fixed gain of 10 for the purpose of solution here. (In a later chapter we shall see the effect of gain variation).

We have the transfer function for this case,

$$\omega(s) = V(s) \cdot \frac{2}{1 + s \cdot 0.088}$$

EXAMPLE 3 – AN ELECTRO-HYDRAULIC POSITION SERVO

So

$$\omega(t) = V(t) \cdot 2 \cdot \left(1 - e^{-\dfrac{t}{0,088}}\right)$$

Figure 2.7 shows the output response of the motor in closed loop. Compare the rate of change of speed and the final value with that for the open loop motor in figure 2.5 above.

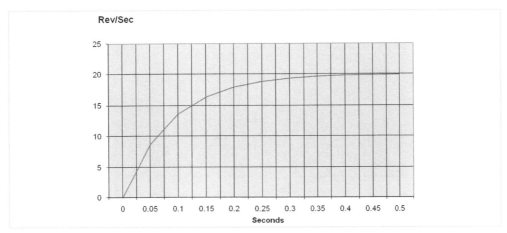

Figure 2.7   Output Response of the DC Servomotor in Closed Loop

Note:
In a practical system, behaviour will not be as predicted in the ideal situation above. The mathematical model does not cater for drive limitations – the maximum motor voltage available is limited by the amplifier supply, as is the available current. A more correct model would include such drive limitation.

Example 3 – An electro-hydraulic position servo

Consider a closed-loop hydraulic position control system as shown in figure 2.8. The heart of the system is the servo-valve, which controls the flow rate of hydraulic fluid as a result of an input current. As current passes into the valve coil, the electro-magnetic effect of the coil acts against a spring to displace the spool away from its central position, thereby opening an orifice for flow into the cylinder. The fluid flow is delivered by a pump, which passes through the valve into the cylinder to produce motion. The system operates in closed loop by measurement of the cylinder position, to produce a feedback voltage. The amplifier compares the feedback voltage with the set-point voltage and the error is used to generate current into the servo-valve. In this manner, whenever there is an error between set-point and feedback, there will always be a current in the servo-valve, hence a flow and motion to reduce that error to zero.

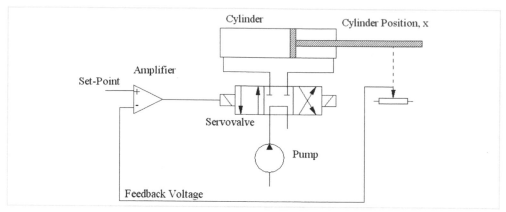

Figure 2.8 *Electro-Hydraulic Position Control*

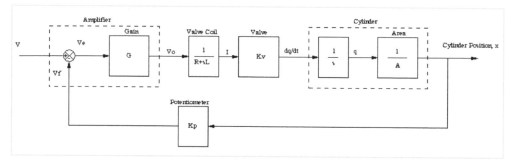

Figure 2.9 *Electro-Hydraulic Position Control Block Diagram*

Using the same block diagram rules, we produce figure 2.9. Note the physical variables shown at the output of each block.

We begin the modelling by consideration of the basic physical relationships, followed by conversion into the Laplace domain and hence completion of the block diagram.

For the amplifier

$$V_o = G \cdot (V - V_f)$$

The servo-valve coil has resistance and inductance, hence

$$V_o = iR + L \cdot \frac{di}{dt}$$

Taking Laplace transforms,

$$V_o(s) = iR + isL = i \cdot (R + sL)$$

EXAMPLE 3 – AN ELECTRO-HYDRAULIC POSITION SERVO

Or, as a transfer function

$$\frac{i}{V_{\mathrm{o}}(s)} = \frac{1}{R + sL}$$

The output of the servo-valve is a flow rate (m^3/sec). The valve is a closed loop system in its own right, considered here for simplicity as controlling flow rate. Hence it is modelled using a simple flow coefficient (m^3/sec per amp), K_{v}.

The hydraulic cylinder is represented as a pure integrator as a convenience to obtain a volume (m^3) from a flow rate (m^3/sec), followed by the surface area of the piston to convert the volume of fluid into a position. (For the cylinder, consider the relationship between flow rate and speed with volume and position).

Finally, the feedback device is presented as a potentiometer position sensor, where feedback voltage is proportional to cylinder position, and is simply represented by a constant K_{p}.

Having considered the physical relationships and made the transformation into the Laplace domain, the block diagram is complete.

The transfer function is obtained as in the previous example by consideration of the forward path and the summing junction.

From the forward path we have,

$$x(s) = V_{\mathrm{e}} \cdot \frac{GK_{\mathrm{v}}}{s \cdot (R + sl) \cdot A}$$

At the summing junction,

$$V_{\mathrm{e}} = V - xK_{\mathrm{p}}$$

So we substitute for V_{e},

$$x(s) = V(s) \cdot \frac{GK_{\mathrm{v}}}{s \cdot (R + sl) \cdot A} - x(s) \cdot \frac{GK_{\mathrm{p}}K_{\mathrm{v}}}{s \cdot (R + sl)A}$$

After re-arrangement, we have the transfer function for the system, which is cast in standard second order transfer function form,

$$x(s) = V(s) \cdot \frac{K}{s^2 + 2\zeta\omega_{\mathrm{n}}s + \omega_{\mathrm{n}}^2}$$

Where

$$K = \frac{GK_v}{LA}; \qquad 2\zeta\omega_n = \frac{R}{L}; \qquad \omega_n^2 = \frac{GK_pK_v}{LA}$$

Presented in this form, the terms within the transfer function have special meaning:

⟹ K is the forward path gain, indicating the gain of the system in steady state conditions;

⟹ ζ ("zeta") is called the damping ratio;

⟹ ω_n is the "natural frequency" of the system, the frequency at which the system would oscillate if there was no damping.

This is most convenient in that standard curves can then be used to describe the output response in the time domain, applicable to any system modelled and presented in this manner. Figure 2.10 shows a family of curves, which are a solution of the output variable against time, for different values of damping ratio.

From the point of view of physical properties, an intuitive approach is useful to relate output performance to system components. Considering the transfer function:

⟹   the resistance and inductance of the coil are significant in the system response since they restrict current into the valve coil and hence rate of change of fluid flow. Under normal circumstances, however, the time constant of the coil would be small compared to that of the cylinder;

⟹   system gain is inversely proportional to cylinder area, as expected, since more flow would be required to obtain the same motion with a larger cylinder area

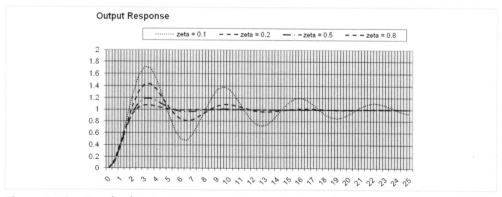

Figure 2.10   *Standard Output Response Curves of a Second Order System*

⟹ the natural frequency is proportional to system gain, indicating that the output would settle faster for higher gains;

⟹ the natural frequency is inversely proportional to cylinder area, since a larger area implies greater volume and hence more flow, taking longer to settle.

In a practical system, parameters would be adjusted to provide a desirable output response. In this case, the only easy adjustment would be the amplifier gain, since all other parameters are hardware components with fixed parameters. In a later chapter, we shall see how system response may be modified using an improved controller.

Modelling steps

To create a model of any physical system, the steps to be taken are exactly the same as in each of the above examples:

⟹ identify the system input variable and the output variable;

⟹ identify each component part and the associated input and output variable of each;

⟹ draw the block diagram, checking that the output from one is the correct input to the next, and that the units match;

⟹ determine the relationships between the input and output of each component;

⟹ take Laplace transforms as appropriate;

⟹ complete the block diagram;

⟹ determine the overall transfer function (Laplace domain);

⟹ solve in the time domain by inverse transformation.

Block diagram rules

Much of the success of the above method depends upon correct identification of component parts. There are some useful rules applicable to the block diagram which aid in the modelling:

⟹ each block is a physical component or parameter of the system;

⟹ each interconnection between blocks is a measurable physical variable.

For neatness and to aid readability, it is also useful to:

⇒ name each component part above the block;

⇒ name each variable between the blocks.

⇒ check that the input and output variables for each block are correct for the particular block component;

⇒ show the transfer function inside the block, correctly relating output to input.

Summary

This chapter has presented a technique to determine a mathematical model for a control system. It has shown how to represent a system by its component parts and to establish the relationships between those components and their input and output variables.

The importance of the Laplace transform has been noted and its usefulness in solution of differential equations, such as commonly encountered in control systems.

Basic rules for creation of a block diagram representation have been described.

The chapter has also presented examples of how a transfer function can be determined easily from the block diagram.

Standard forms of first and second order systems with typical time domain response have been presented.

3
Time Response Techniques

We have considered in the previous chapter on system modelling the practical components in a system and used block diagram representation to aid in the derivation of a transfer function for the system.

We have also observed that the time response can be determined by solution of the transfer function with a given input stimulus. Generally, it is the time response which is of most interest, in particular for observation of stability, overshoot and error.

Time response is usually analysed by determination of the output of the system in response to a "step input" signal, to determine how the system settles to a new operating point and how it will cope with disturbances. A "unit step" is a step input with a magnitude of 1. Alternatively, a "ramp input" may be used to determine how well the system is able to follow a changing input. Figure 3.1 shows these input types diagrammatically.

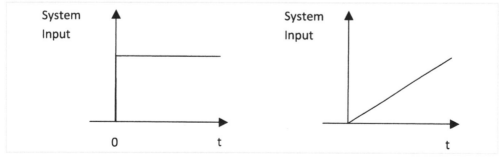

Figure 3.1   *Step and ramp input signals*

Time Domain Solution

The system model is usually derived in the Laplace domain, since it is easier to handle the differential equations algebraically and then to cast the transfer function into a standard form. The time response will be examine further by development of the time solution. Consider the general case first order transfer function for a system with input X and output Y, expressed in the Laplace domain

$$\frac{Y}{X(s)} = \frac{K}{1 + sT}$$

Re-iterating the time solution presented earlier, it is necessary to define the input signal in the Laplace domain, determine an expression for the output and then convert back to the time domain.

For a unit step applied at $t = 0$, the output can therefore be expressed

$$Y(s) = \left(\frac{1}{s}\right) \cdot \frac{K}{1 + sT}$$

yielding the time domain solution,

$$Y(t) = K \cdot \left(1 - e^{-\frac{t}{T}}\right)$$

We hinted earlier at the significance of the time constant T. Consider then the output of the system for $K = 1$, at significant points in time,

$t = 0$	the output will be zero
$t = T$	since $t/T = 1$, the term $(1 - e^{-t/T})$ will equal 0.632, ie the output will have risen from zero to 63.2% of its final value in one time constant period
$t = 5T$	the term $(1 - e^{-t/T})$ will be very close to unity, ie the output will have very nearly reached its final value after 5 time constant periods
$t = \infty$	the output will have settled at its final value

The general case first order time response can then be illustrated as in figure 3.2, showing the above conditions,

For systems of any order, the solution procedure would be the same. Recall the standard output curves for the second order system time solution shown again in figure 3.3. All systems of order 2 or greater will exhibit this form of response. Note however, that for many practical applications, the ideal output response will be very similar to that shown in figure 3.2, since it is required to approach the desired output value as fast as possible, but without overshoot.

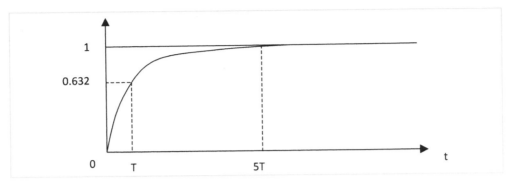

Figure 3.2 *General case first order time response*

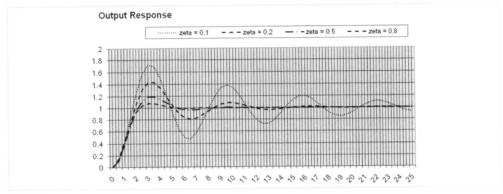

Figure 3.3 *Normalised time domain response*

A system is said to be "critically damped" when the system is tuned (normally by forward path amplifier gain adjustment) such that the output response achieves the steady state just on the verge of overshoot.

The order of the system is determined by the number of "energy storage devices", ie components of the system which introduce a differential term into the transfer function (capacitors, inductors, hydraulic cylinders, inertial load etc). The relative time constants of these components contribute towards the time response and overshoot characteristics.

The same time domain solutions could be determined for a ramp input (eg for a machine tool contour-following system, to determine the following error).

Steady State Error

Consider the dc motor speed control system in figure 3.4. The motor is driven by a power amplifier, with feedback from a tacho-generator. The drive voltage to the motor depends upon amplifier gain A, and the difference between the input and feedback voltages.

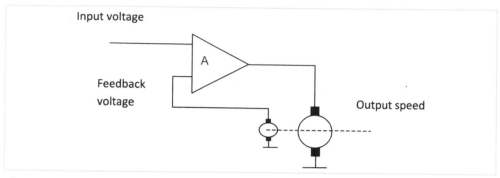

Figure 3.4 *Motor speed control*

In this system, the feedback voltage will never equal the input voltage, since there must always be an error signal in order to produce an output from the amplifier to drive the motor. The only adjustment available here is the amplifier gain. It follows that the amplifier gain may be increased to reduce the error, but there will be a limit to the practical value of A before system instability occurs. Increasing gain will also reduce the response time of the system, and affect the shape of the output response curve as above. This type of control is called "Proportional" because the output actuation signal is proportional to the error.

From the time domain viewpoint, we can illustrate the response of the motor speed to a step change in input voltage in figure 3.5.

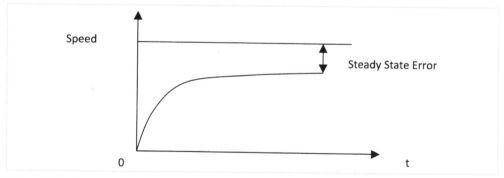

Figure 3.5 *Motor output speed response*

The "steady state error" is the difference between the desired output and the actual output values after the transient has expired ie the output is in a steady state. The error can be determined from the transfer function. For example, for the first order system we have,

$$Y(s) = \frac{X(s)K}{1 + sT}$$

We can apply the "Final Value Theorem" to determine the steady state output (ie final value). Since the "s" operator represents time-changing (differential) terms, and is associated with system component time constants, it follows that the terms will have no effect in the steady state when time differentials will have ceased. By ignoring the "s" terms in the transfer function (ie making s → 0), the final value is obtained. For the above, we have

$$Y = X \cdot \frac{K}{1}$$

So the output is as expected, being the input multiplied by the system (closed loop) gain. The same technique may be applied to higher order systems to determine the steady state output and hence error.

Controllers

A controller may be used to add functions in the forward or feedback path to improve the time response. Consider again the motor speed control system in figure 3.4, but with an integrator in the forward path. The modified control system is shown in figure 3.6.

The feedback voltage is compared with the input voltage in the same way, and the speed error determined. The output of the error amplifier however, is passed to the input of an integrator (which has the properties of integration in the normal mathematical sense) and can be described in practical terms as follows,

Integrator Input	Integrator Output
0	Remains steady
Positive	Ramps Positive
Negative	Ramps Negative

Thus, while ever there is an error between input and feedback voltages, the error amplifier output will be non-zero and the output will ramp in the appropriate direction to change the motor speed to reduce that error to zero. If the error is zero, then the integrator output remains constant so the drive voltage to the motor is maintained at the present level, holding the motor speed constant. For disturbances in the load causing a speed change, or for changes in the input voltage, an error will be produced thereby producing a ramp in the integrator output to correct the motor drive voltage and compensate for that disturbance.

This is termed "Integral Action" and is useful in the cancellation of error. The drawback is that the system stability is reduced, since the integrator adds an extra order to the transfer function and delays the output response.

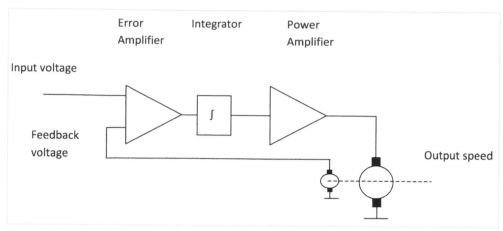

Figure 3.6   *Modified motor speed control*

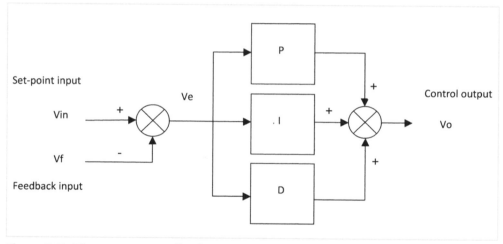

Figure 3.7   *Three term controller functional diagram*

Addition of integral action produces oscillations in the output which may be undesirable, even if they eventually cease to leave the output in a stable, correct steady state. A further term can be added to compensate for oscillation or rapid changes in the output. By detection of the rate of change of error, an extra correction can be introduced to cancel out such changes. This additional component is termed "derivative action", since it operates with the differential of the error signal.

Hence the "3 term controller", which finds application in a multitude of control systems, providing a means to optimise system performance and tune the output response. Proportional, integral and derivative terms are summed to produce the output signal. The effect of each term can be adjusted to "tune" the system for the desired output response. Figure 3.7 shows a 3 term controller functional diagram.

The controller function can be described

$$V_o = PV_e + I\int V_e + D \cdot \frac{V_e}{dt}$$

Where the error voltage

$$V_e = V_{in} - V_f$$

P, I and D are multipliers to adjust the relative amount of each term added to the output signal.

Summary

This chapter has considered the time response of a control system and noted its salient features.

It has also considered the use of 3 term control to tune the system output response.

4
Frequency Response Techniques

In this chapter, we shall consider performance of the system to ac input signals. We shall observe the effect of increasing frequency, ie to determine the frequency response of the system, and to note the relationship with the physical components.

Frequency Response of an RC Network

Let us consider the same example of a simple RC network, in order that the frequency response can be evaluated and comparisons drawn with the time response determined previously. The network is shown again in figure 4.1 with applied voltage V_{in}, resistance R, and capacitance C.

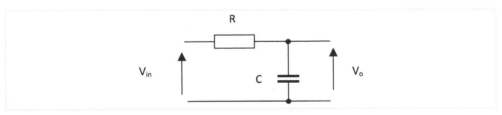

Figure 4.1   RC Network

The transfer function model for the network, describing V_0 in terms of V_{in} and the component parts, was derived using Laplace representation for eventual solution of the differential equation in the time domain,

$$V_0 = V_{in} \cdot \frac{1}{1 + sRC}$$

Or

$$\frac{V_0}{V_{in}} = \frac{K}{1 + sT}$$

Where $K = 1$ and $T = RC$

To consider how the network would behave under ac input stimulus, we apply similar techniques, but must consider the effects of frequency on the system components. In this case, we again express the output voltage in terms of the input voltage and component parameters. Considering the network as a potential divider, the output voltage can be determined as a fraction of capacitor reactance out of the total, ie

$$V_\mathrm{o} = V_\mathrm{in} \cdot \frac{X_\mathrm{C}}{R + X_\mathrm{C}}$$

Where X_C is the reactance of the capacitor, given by

$$X_\mathrm{C} = \frac{1}{2\pi f C}$$

(ie the reactance of the capacitor reduces with increasing frequency). For frequency response analysis, we normally work with radian/second as the unit of frequency instead of Hz, so remembering that $\omega = 2\pi f$, we have

$$X_c = \frac{1}{\omega C}$$

and

$$V_\mathrm{o} = \frac{V_\mathrm{in} \cdot \left(\dfrac{1}{\omega C}\right)}{R + \left(\dfrac{1}{\omega C}\right)}$$

or

$$V_\mathrm{o} = V_\mathrm{in} \cdot \frac{1}{1 + \omega C R}$$

so

$$G(\omega) = \frac{1}{1 + \omega C R}$$

The RC network is often referred to as a simple lag, since the output voltage lags behind the input. (Consider the physical properties of a capacitor, where current leads voltage, so the change in output voltage is "delayed" with respect to the input. Phase shift is therefore negative).

There are then two component parts to the frequency response transfer function:

⬛⬛➡   a "gain" or "magnitude", the ratio of output voltage to input voltage

$$\left|G(\omega)\right| = (1 + (\omega C R)^2)^{-0.5}$$

⬛⬛➡   and a phase angle, the lag between output and input

$$\theta(\omega) = -\tan^{-1} \omega C R$$

The magnitude and phase can be represented on a plot as shown in figure 4.2, referred to as a "Polar plot" or "R,θ" diagram. At low frequencies, $\omega \rightarrow 0$, so the magnitude will be 1 and the phase shift zero. At high frequencies, $\omega \rightarrow \infty$, so the magnitude will be zero and the phase shift 90 degrees.

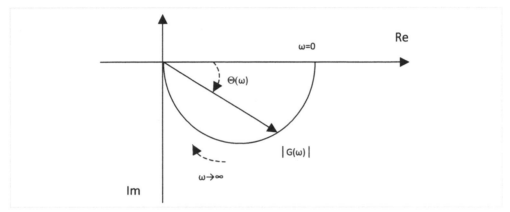

Figure 4.2   *Polar plot of gain and phase for the RC network*

We refer to polar plots as "magnitude and angle" or "Real and Imaginary", given the mathematical approach. For frequency response purposes, it is more usual to refer to "gain and phase" from a signal processing viewpoint. For all intents and purposes, the polar plot and frequency response diagrams convey the same information.

Gain and phase can therefore be calculated against frequency and represented on a "Bode Diagram", as shown in figure 4.3 (H. W. Bode developed much of the work on frequency response during the 1920s). Gain is normally expressed in dB which is a logarithmic expression of magnitude, the convenience being that the overall magnitude of a system can be determined by summing the contribution of each stage, ie a vertical shift of the plot on the same axes. Further, the plot is usually produced against a logarithmic frequency scale to simplify observation over a large frequency range.

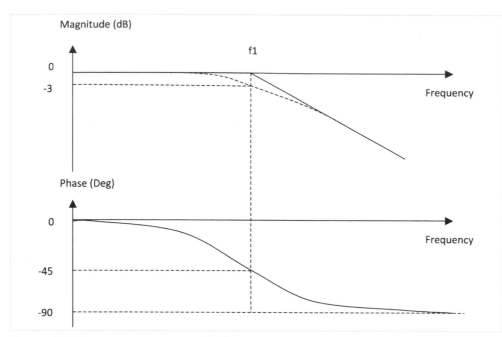

Figure 4.3 *Frequency response Bode diagram*

Gain is calculated in dB using the expression

$$Gain(dB) = 20 \cdot \log_{10} |G(j\omega)|$$

So a gain of 1 is a gain of 0 dB.

Frequency response approximations

Consider again the expression for the magnitude,

$$|G(\omega)| = (1 + (\omega C R)^2)^{-0.5}$$

Note that when the frequency $\omega = 1 / RC$, the magnitude will have fallen to 0.707 (ie $1/\sqrt{2}$, or –3 dB) and the phase shift will be 45 degrees. This point is marked as f_1 on the frequency response plots above. This particular frequency is significant, and is referred to as the "break frequency" or the "system "bandwidth". Note the relationship between the break frequency and the time response (remember from an earlier chapter that the time response of the system is characterised by the "time constant").

For the RC network, the time constant $T = RC$ and the break frequency $\omega = 1/RC$.

Consider then three parts of the frequency response plot:

⏩ at low frequencies the gain is the same as the dc gain (ie $\omega = 0$) This can be determined by inspection of the frequency response transfer function and ignoring all ω terms, since $\omega = 0$;

⏩ at the break frequency, the gain is −3 dB and the phase shift 45 degrees;

⏩ at higher frequencies, the gain falls off and becomes asymptotic to −20 dB per decade, and phase shift approaches 90 degrees.

It therefore becomes a simple task to draw the frequency response curve by inspection, using straight line approximations as shown in the figure.

Higher order systems

For higher order systems, the frequency response can be determined in the same way. Each "order" has a magnitude and phase contribution as above, ie

System order	Gain fall-off (dB/decade)	Maximum phase shift (degree)
1st	−20	90
2nd	−40	180
3rd	−60	270

It becomes apparent that the frequency response is useful in stability assessment, since the critical condition of "loop gain = −1" may be identified. It is worth noting at this point that a low order system has inherently higher stability than one of higher order.

Since each order contributes a further 90 degrees of phase shift, the higher the order, the more chance there will be of creating the unstable positive feedback condition. In theory, first and second order systems can never become unstable, since the phase shift can never exceed 180 degrees.

Comparison with time response

Consider again the general case first order transfer function in frequency response terms,

$$G(j\omega) = \frac{1}{1 + j\omega T}$$

Compare it with the transfer function developed earlier in the Laplace domain,

$$G(s) = \frac{K}{1 + sT}$$

Note the similarity, in that conversion between frequency domain and Laplace domain is simply a case of making the substitution $s = j\omega$.

As expected, the time response and the frequency response are functions of the component parts of the overall system, and are directly related as we have observed above.

Poles and Zeroes

So far we have considered a first order lag with a transfer function of the form

$$G(\omega) = \frac{1}{1 + \omega T}$$

Within a control system, each phase lag component would introduce a further term on the denominator of the transfer function, whereas each phase lead component would introduce a term on the numerator. Denominator terms are referred to as "poles" and numerator terms are referred to as "zeroes". Each pole contributes up to 90 degrees of phase lag, while each zero contributes up to 90 degrees of phase lead.

The general case transfer function (expressed in the Laplace domain) may be presented,

$$G(s) = \frac{K(s + z_1)(s + z_2)(s + z_3)...}{(s + p_1)(s + p_2)(s + p_3)...}$$

Earlier we derived the closed loop transfer function

$$y = x \cdot \frac{G}{1 + GH}$$

Applying a similar analysis as above, we can represent the system characteristic equation in either frequency response or Laplace domain. The roots of the characteristic equation are the poles and zeroes of the system, providing an excellent tool for control system stability analysis.

Stability and compensation

We have seen that the characteristic equation contains all control system parameters, and we are aware of the condition to be avoided when $GH = -1$, ie a phase shift of 180 degrees and a loop gain of 1. We have also observed that a control system may have phase lead or phase lag components.

It follows therefore that a system can be compensated by appropriate use of phase lead networks to cancel the effects of phase lag, and therefore improve system stability. If we can add a phase lead parameter to cancel out the effects of a phase lag, we can maintain a stable system by preventing the phase shift from ever approaching 180 degrees.

Consider a machine tool electro-hydraulic positioning system represented in figure 4.4, where a position sensor provides feedback via K_f to a controller to set the tool position. The hydraulic cylinder is effectively a pure integrator contributing a pole and hence a fixed phase shift of 90 degrees. Other terms in the system contribute to produce a third order system.

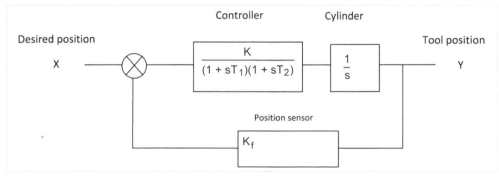

Figure 4.4 *Electro-hydraulic position control system*

A full analysis could be carried out to model the system, produce the transfer function and graph the system frequency response. We would expect the phase angle to be in excess of 180 degrees (ie up to 270 degrees for the third order system) and we could identify a frequency range over which the system would be unstable. To compensate for the instability, it is necessary to add a phase lead. Choice of such a compensator requires practical application, in that we must choose one of the system poles to be cancelled by our addition of a zero. Ideally, we should choose to cancel the "slowest" pole (ie the longest time constant) to produce an overall faster system. Whilst that is simple in theoretical terms, the system contains a pure integrator in the hydraulic cylinder, and in practical terms the speed of response will be limited by the ability of the pump to deliver oil into that cylinder. (It is a mistake to believe that any system can necessarily be compensated in this way, since there will always be practical limitations which may not be achieveable, in the manner in which a theoretical analysis might suggest, as highlighted in this example).

To compensate this system, a more practical solution would be to cancel one of the higher frequency poles by addition of a phase lead in the controller, as shown in figure 4.5. A zero is added with time constant T_c chosen to cancel one of the poles at T_1 or T_2, and therefore adjust the frequency response characteristic.

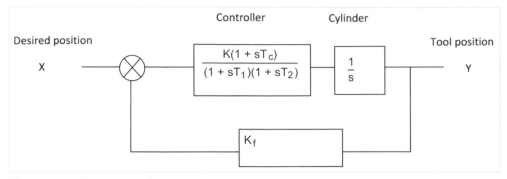

Figure 4.5 *Compensated system*

The compensation described above is achieved by addition of components in the forward path. Similar results can be achieved by compensation in the feedback path, since it forms part of the characteristic equation. Consider a common solution to this particular problem (and in motor speed control) by the addition of "rate feedback", ie a derivative term in the loop gain, which has the same effect of introducing phase lead and a zero to the characteristic equation. Rate feedback is effectively the feedback of a speed component, which by definition is the derivative of position. It is commonly used in positioning systems to provide improved stability. Figure 4.6 shows the same electro-hydraulic system with the addition of rate feedback. The original controller can be used (without the need for the compensating lead factor) since the compensation is inherent in the speed sensor.

In derivation of the transfer function, the rate feedback appears as a term (sY), ie dY/dt, and therefore appears in the numerator rather than the denominator, ie a system zero.

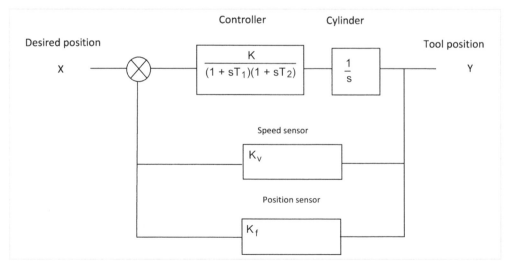

Figure 4.6 *Compensated system (rate feedback)*

System compensation is usually achieved by addition of a 3 term controller, as discussed in the chapter on time response. From the frequency response and stability point of view,

Integral term	adds a pole to the transfer function
	introduces up to 90 degrees of additional phase lag
	reduces system stability

Derivative term	adds a zero to the transfer function
	introduces up to 90 degrees of additional phase lead
	improves system stability

Summary

This chapter has considered the response of a control system to inputs of varying frequency, developing the frequency response approach and appropriate graphical representation.

We have considered system stability based upon loop gain and phase shift against frequency. We have also considered how a system might be compensated to improve stability by means of phase lead components.

5
System Simulation

Why simulate

For most systems, it is the time domain response in which we are interested, viewed as a trend against time for a change in input. Having modelled the system and reached a time domain solution, it is normally a simple task to calculate the output for a given input.

In many cases, it is useful to determine the output response of a system without having access to the system itself. For example

➠ before manufacture, when the system is not built

➠ a system is in continuous production and is therefore not available for experimentation

➠ observation of system response as a result of component or parameter change ("What if" scenarios)

➠ other practical or cost restraints

A major benefit of simulation is that behaviour can be analysed and the effects of parameter changes noted without using the actual system and causing possible interference to production. Further, for new systems, the simulation exercise is valuable for choice of controller, system settings, tuning and performance. Once a suitable model has been obtained, it remains to choose a simulation technique which will produce the desired output and allow the required investigation.

This chapter presents different methods for system simulation. In particular, the emphasis is upon simulations which are easily programmed, so that all modelling, simulation and system analysis may be performed entirely at the desktop. The methods presented form the basis upon which commercially available simulation packages have been developed.

Simulation methods

Simulation is in itself a wide subject area. We shall focus on three of the more common methods, all of which are readily available:

Spreadsheet	Universally available, ready computation and easy graphing, useful for time domain solution and visualisation, but becomes clumsy if several variable output responses are required
Programming	For the more serious user, where a high level language is used to represent the system and deliver more comprehensive results. This method requires far more effort on the part of the user, risks dedication to a particular choice of system, but has the ability to produce a wider range of output information
Packages	There is a wide range of system simulation packages available, ranging from those with high visual content in a "pick and go" environment, to dedicated simulation programming languages requiring programming knowledge. The packages generally make system simulation easier by providing ready-made libraries of common functions, including a range of input stimulation waveforms, standard models of engineering components, and a range of graphical output forms.

In this chapter, we shall investigate the use of a spreadsheet as a simple solution, and then develop a common technique for use in a high level programming language. We shall simulate a first order system to develop the background and produce the time response.

Spreadsheet simulation

Simulation using a spreadsheet is one of the easiest and widely available forms of problem solution and is generally available on all personal computing platforms. Although simplistic in approach, spreadsheets do incorporate the mathematical functions necessary and have a powerful set of graphing tools. For our purposes, we will use a spreadsheet just for solution of the time response, although frequency response may be just as easily included.

As an example, consider the RC network modelled in an earlier chapter. An expression for the output voltage as a function of time was obtained, as a result of a step input in applied voltage, V_{in},

$$V_o(t) = V_{in}(t) \cdot \left(1 - e^{-\frac{t}{RC}}\right)$$

Figure 5.1 shows a simple spreadsheet example, where values for R, C may be entered. The time constant RC is calculated, and the equation solved using the spreadsheet EXP function (which raises e to a specified power).

	A	B	C	D
1	RC Network Response			
2				
3				
4	R	1000.00	Ohms	
5	C	0.001	Farad	
6				
7	T	1.00		
8				
9	Time		Vo	
10	0		0.00	
11	0.5		0.39	
12	1		0.63	
13	1.5		0.78	
14	2		0.86	
15	2.5		0.92	
16	3		0.95	
17	3.5		0.97	
18	4		0.98	
19	4.5		0.99	
20	5		0.99	
21				
22				

Figure 5.1   Spreadsheet simulation

To produce the output response, a time base is required, with a period and interval chosen to suit the expected system performance. Cells A10 through A20 are easily filled using the "Fill Series" spreadsheet operation, specifying an appropriate step size and end value. In this example, the output is calculated over a 5 second period at a 0.5 second interval.

In the figure, T is calculated in cell B7. Cell B10 contains the solution expression

```
= (1 - EXP(-A10 / $B$7))
```

The "Fill Down" spreadsheet operation may be used to copy the function to cells below to cover the time period required.

Although the example is simple, care must be taken with cell absolute and relative addressing. The values for R and C are held in *absolute* cell references B4 and B5 respectively. The time constant calculation in cell B7 refers explicitly to cells B4 and B5 (=B4*B5).

Cells B11 through B20 contain the same solution expression as above, but have an *absolute* reference to cell B7 (time constant, T) and a *relative* reference to the time values in A10 through A20.

In the example spreadsheet shown, absolute references are made by placing a "$" before the cell reference row and column, ie the time constant T, is referenced by B7. Cells B10 through B20 therefore contain

```
= $B$9 * (1 - EXP(-A10 / $B$7))
= $B$9 * (1 - EXP(-A11 / $B$7))
= $B$9 * (1 - EXP(-A12 / $B$7))
   . . .
```

Note the absolute reference to the time constant, whilst the time reference is relative, taking a time value from each row.

To graph the response, the "Insert Chart" operation is used, and the data ranges chosen such that the time values (column A) are used as the chart X series data and the "Vo" values are used as the chart Y series data values.

Having created the spreadsheet, it is easy to change values for R and C and immediately observe the output response.

Choice of time-base can be a difficult aspect of simulation programming, but a useful approach is to consider a time interval from $t = 0$ to $t = 5T$ (ie "5 time constants", the time in which the output will be within 99% of its final value). The time step should be chosen to give sufficient data points over the period of interest – typically a minimum of 10 points and a maximum of 50.

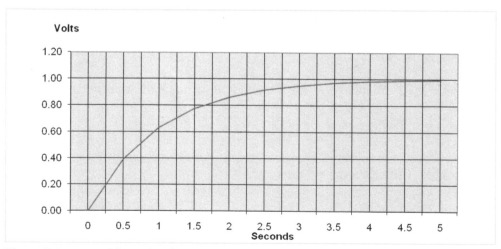

Figure 5.2   Spreadsheet simulation result

In the example, using a 1 KΩ resistor and 1000 μF capacitor, the time constant would be 1 second, so a time-base of 5 seconds was used. A time step of 0.5 second yielded 11 data points over the simulation period. Figure 5.2 shows the resulting plot. Ideally, more points should be taken to improve definition, since the output curve is not as smooth as might be desired.

The simulation relies upon the mathematical model of the system being accurate, but also that the solution technique is producing the correct output. It is useful to prove operation by testing the output for a known input, or checking some other aspect(s) of the results. In this simple example, it is sufficient to observe that

➠   the output curve follows a first order response, (as expected);

➠   the final value is 1 volt, (as expected for a 1 volt input);

➠   the output is 0.63 volts at $t = 1$ second (as expected, since we know that the
-    output should be 63% of the final value at $t = T$).

We can therefore be satisfied that the simulation is producing a correct representation of the system and carry on to observe the effects of other inputs or parameter changes.

Programming for simulation

A spreadsheet offers easy creation and graphing for simulation exercises, but becomes significantly more cumbersome as the system to be simulated becomes more complex, of higher order or more output information is required. Particularly, cell references and cell calculations can be difficult to handle and document. For this reason, it is often useful to use a high level programming language for the simulation data entry and calculations. Graphing may be more difficult, since more effort is required to produce a convenient output display. An alternative is to write data to a disc file and use an alternative package for graphing purposes.

Techniques are available for system simulation using high level languages. Two methods are presented here, both of which can be repeated easily on a PC. The examples presented are given in C# code, but any other high level programming language could be used. The two methods presented are called

    Direct programming

and

    Euler integration

Direct Programming

Direct programming is essentially to solve the time response in a single line of programme, using a loop to control the required time interval and period. Figure 5.3 shows a C# code segment to solve the same RC network time response as in the previous example.

```
public float Vin;
public float T;
public float K;
public float dt;
public float time_elapsed;
public float period;
public float Vo;

  while (time_elapsed < period)
  {
    Vo = Vin * (1-exp-(time_elapsed/T));
    time_elapsed = time_elapsed + dt;
  }
```

Figure 5.3   C# code segment for time solution

Whichever programming language is chosen, the sequence of events will be the same, and the approach very similar. In the C# example of figure 5.3, the variables used in the calculation are declared, then the simulation is executed as a "while" loop, using a time step "dt" until the "time elapsed" reaches the desired simulation period.

It is good practice in such programming to use variable names which relate directly to the system variables. From the simulation point of view, it is necessary to ensure that sufficient calculation points are taken over the simulation period to define the output appropriately. In the example above, the code requires modification to write output values to an array, to a text box for display or to disc.

Since this technique is merely the calculation of the time response solution, programming is simple, but the same checks should be performed to ensure that the output is an accurate representation of how the system would perform.

It is a simple matter to add additional code to determine other system variables (eg we could solve for the current in the network above to observe lag effects). Similarly, frequency response could be determined, but an additional loop would be required to calculate gain and phase.

Euler integration

An alternative (and possibly more interesting) technique is to use integrators within the simulation, the outputs of which represent directly the physical variables in the system. The technique was originally developed to suit analogue computers using electronic integrator modules, but has since returned to popularity with the "State Space" description of systems in modern control theory and application to numerical solution. The description is a little more cumbersome initially, but presents a most convenient means for digital computer solution.

For simplicity, we begin with the standard first order system, for which we have the transfer function

$$\frac{y}{x(s)} = \frac{K}{1+sT}$$

To proceed, we present it in a different form by "separation of the highest derivative". (Remember that the Laplace operator "s" represents the differential operator, d/dt). We have then,

$$y(1+sT) = Kx$$

From which

$$ysT = Kx - y$$

So

$$sy = \frac{K}{T}x - \frac{1}{T}y .$$

The term "sy" is the Laplace representation of dy/dt, being the differentiation of the output variable y with respect to time. We can produce a diagram for the above representation based upon an integrator, the input to which would be "sy" and the output from which would be the system output variable, y. Figure 5.4 (next page) shows this representation diagrammatically.

Note that the input to the integrator is the "highest derivative", dy/dt , as described in the equation as a function of input x, output y, and the system parameters K and T. The integrator has a correct relation between input and output, ie input dy/dt and output y. In this form, the system could be simulated directly on an analogue computer, where a single integrator block with summing junction would be used, and two potentiometers to represent variables K/T and $1/T$.

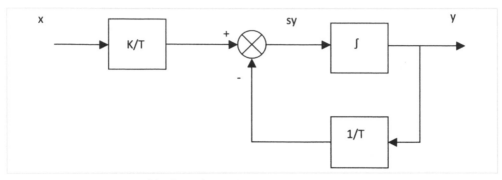

Figure 5.4 *Separation of highest derivative*

We shall proceed however to numerical simulation on a PC. To perform the integration, we shall adopt a technique called "Euler's Approximation".

> No proof or explanation of this technique is within the scope of this text. There is much documentation on numerical simulation and solution techniques, especially for solution on digital computer systems. The reader is encouraged to consult the later section on "Further reading" and other sources, where there is a vast array of material regarding integration techniques, numerical solution of differential equations, performance, accuracy and error analysis etc.

For the purpose of this text we shall accept the practical description of the manner in which the integrator operates, as presented in the chapter on "Time Response Techniques", ie

Integrator Input	Integrator Output
0	Remains steady
Positive	Ramps Positive
Negative	Ramps Negative

This behaviour is described by an algorithm suitable for programming and numerical solution, where the integrator output is calculated at each programme loop. Each programme loop represents one time increment or time step, beginning at zero and increasing until the end of the simulation period. We have then an expression to determine the integrator output at the next time step,

$$y_{n+1} = y_n + (sy \cdot h)$$

Where y_{n+1} is the integrator output determined from the current value (y_n) updated by an increment obtained by multiplication of the input (sy) and the time step. Note how this simple calculation matches the description of integrator operation in the table above.

The description is now complete and figure 5.5 presents a C# code segment to solve the time response for the first order system.

```
public float x;
public float T;
public float K;
public float y;
public float sy;
public float dt;
public float time_elapsed;
public float period;

  while (time_elapsed < period)
  {
    sy =( x * K / T) - (y / T);
    y = y + (sy * dt);
    time_elapsed = time_elapsed + dt;
  }
```

Figure 5.5   C# code segment, first order simulation by Euler integration technique

After the variable declarations, the simulation is executed in a programme loop with time step dt, until elapsed time reaches the end of a fixed period. The output variable "y" could be written to an array or to disc for later display and visualisation.

This technique is easily extended to higher order systems by following the same methodology. Consider a second order system with input x and output y,

$$y(s) = x(s) \cdot \frac{K}{s^2 + 2\zeta\omega_n + \omega_n^2}$$

Separating the highest derivative (s^2),

$$s^2 y + 2\zeta\omega_n s y + \omega_n^2 y = K x$$

So

$$s^2 y = K x - 2\zeta\omega_n s y - \omega_n^2 y$$

Figure 5.6 (next page) shows the system as a series of integrators.

Note that the second order system is represented by two integrators. Indeed, for any system the number of integrators required will equal the system order.

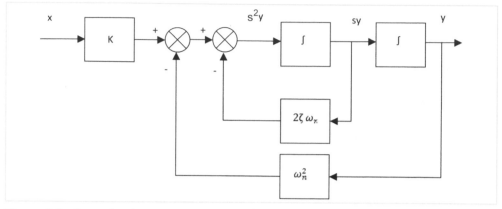

Figure 5.6 *Second order system representation*

Programming follows the same steps as for the first order example, ie a line of code to define the input to the first integrator, followed by a line for each integrator.

Systems of higher order may be represented in the same manner. Simulation using this technique has distinct advantages, but there are drawbacks. The following points are worthy of note:

➠   derivatives of the output variable are directly available from the simulation and may easily be viewed against time. For a position control system, this would be particularly useful, since the derivatives would be speed and acceleration. For other variables, the second or higher derivatives may not convey such useful practical meaning;

➠   the time interval must be carefully chosen, since the integration technique can fail. Too large an interval causes output instability, too small an interval introduces increasing numerical error. A rule of thumb is to begin with an interval one-tenth of the shortest system time constant.

Figure 5.7 presents a C# code segment to solve the time response for the second order system. Note the similarity with the first order code, in that the first line determines the input to the first integrator, while successive lines deal with each following integrator.

Specialist packages

Simulation is a useful tool within any engineering discipline, and in many other areas where rules and data are available to build a model. If a system obeys physical laws or can be represented numerically, then a model can be derived. Alternatively, a system may not obey such deterministic laws, but may have statistical data, historical evidence or other rules by which a model can be created for simulation.

```
public float x;
public float K;
public float Zeta;
public float wn;
public float Vo;
public float y;
public float sy;
public float ssy;

public float dt;
public float time_elapsed;
public float period;

  while (time_elapsed < period)
  {
    ssy =(x * K) - (2 * Zeta * wn * sy) - (wn * wn * y);
    sy = sy + (ssy * dt);
    y = y + (sy * dt);
    time_elapsed = time_elapsed + dt;
  }
```

Figure 5.7 C# code segment, second order simulation by Euler integration technique

Not surprisingly, several specialist packages are available for system simulation. For our purposes, they will fall into one of three categories:

➤ general purpose mathematical modelling and solving tools, where any system represented by mathematical description can be defined and observed;

➤ simulation tools intended expressly for electronic and control system simulation;

➤ simulation tools intended for other physical analysis purposes (such as finite element modelling of mechanical properties, heat transfer, material deformation under load, etc).

The area is beyond the scope of this text and the reader is referred to further reading and additional material.

Summary

This chapter has given an insight into the usefulness of system simulation. Examples have been considered using spreadsheet and C# code. An introduction to Euler techniques has been given for simulation of systems of higher order, with a C# code sample.

6
Instrumentation

The Instrumentation System

The measurement of physical variables is essential if that variable is to be controlled. The instrumentation system includes

→ a sensor to detect the variable to be measured

→ processing of the signal to produce a standard level or use-able output

→ a display or recording device

Figure 6.1 shows the basic measurement system architecture. For use in a control system, the sensor and processing make up the feedback path, producing a standard signal level (eg 0 – 10 V) for connection into the controller.

For use in a display or recording system, the output form is chosen to suit the desired purpose, (eg as a simple read-out display, bar chart or trend). In some display and recording applications it is more useful to apply statistical processing techniques to condense the data into a more understandable or presentable form.

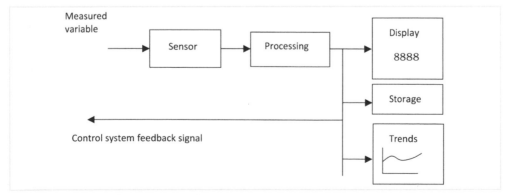

Figure 6.1   General instrumentation system

Whatever the purpose of the measurement, it is useful to record the data for later viewing of historical trends.

This chapter presents an overview of sensor types for measurement of a range of physical variables. Most of the chapter is concerned with signal processing, conversion, transmission and storage.

Specification

To specify an instrumentation system it is necessary to know the purpose of the output signal and the characteristics of the variable to be measured, including

▶ Range of measurement

▶ Environment, feasibility of installation, reliability

▶ Output signal type

▶ Speed of response required (frequency response, rate of change of the variable)

▶ Continuous or discrete data

▶ Sensitivity (the smallest change which can be detected)

▶ Resolution (definition of measurement, the "weight" of a one bit change in digital systems)

▶ Accuracy ("closeness to the truth")

Sensors

There is a huge range of physical variables which we may measure for various purposes in process control, manufacturing, medical, automobile and aerospace applications, amongst many others. The following figures present some of the more commonly measured variables and details the type of sensing element normally used.

Note

▶ the following is by no means exhaustive. Sensor technology is advancing rapidly and many different types exist for each physical variable. The tables merely present some of the most common types of industrial grade sensing technology.

➠ the difference between direct measurement and inferred measurement. Direct measurement is where the instrument is immediately sensitive to changes in the measured variable; inferred measurement is where a different variable is used to sense the desired measurement (refer to tables for examples)

The first table shows "fluid" variables, ie those associated with liquid or heat flow, typical in hydraulic or temperature control systems.

The second table shows "mechanical" variables, ie those associated with motion, typical in machine tools, robotics, guided vehicles etc.

Variable	Type	Sensing element
Temperature	Thermocouple	Junction of two different metals
	PT100	Resistance wire
Pressure	Diapraghm	strain gauge
	Piezoelectric	crystal deformation
Flow	Impellor	Pulse counting
	Pitot tube	
	Venturi or orifice	Pressure drop across a restriction
	Ultrasonic	Time-of-flight through transit media
Level	Capacitive	Change in capacitance between concentric tubes
	Ultrasonic	Time-of-flight sensor to level

Figure 6.2 "Fluid" Variables

Variable	Type	Sensing element
Force	Load cell	strain gauge
	Compressive	spring / potentiometric
Position	Potentiometric	resistance track
	Magneto-restrictive	time-of-flight pulse in waveguide
	Encoder	engraved disc / light source, pulse count
Speed	Tacho-generator	induced voltage
	Pulse counting	gear tooth / inductive proximity sensor
	Optical	engraved disc / light source pulse frequency
Acceleration	Mass	mass-spring-damper potentiometric

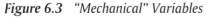

Figure 6.3 "Mechanical" Variables

Data Processing and Transmission

Data from a particular sensor will require to be transmitted to a display instrument or to the input of a processor. The original signal is referred to as "raw data" and will require some form of processing before presentation and use. The signal processing required depends upon several factors, including:

⟹   the nature of the measured variable (rate of change, absolute value / range, frequency range);

⟹   environment (influence of noise);

⟹   distance to be transmitted;

⟹   sampling rate;

⟹   etc.

The signal may be processed in analogue form, typically within the sensor, to convert it to a standard industrial level (0–10 volts, 4–20 mA etc). Further processing may be necessary to remove noise and then to scale the value to a particular engineering unit for meaningful display. In computer applications, processing may be performed within software. This section considers various common signal processing requirements and how they are implemented in analogue and digital systems.

Processing – Analogue

Level conversion

The most common processing required for analogue signals is to convert them to a standard level for connection into another device, such as a display unit, PLC or recorder. The sensing element will require electrical excitation and produce a signal as a result of the physical variable to which it responds. That signal will often require amplification to a useful level, and conversion to an industrial standard. The most commonly used standard signal levels are 0 – 10 Volts, 0 – 10 milliamps and 4 – 20 milliamps.

Current signals (eg 4 – 20 mA) are common in the process industries, since they are inherently low impedance, making them impervious to noise, and the signal can be transmitted over the relatively long distances typical of larger process plant installations. In a correctly designed circuit, the current is controlled in a closed loop, so that the resistance of the cable between source and destination does not affect the received signal. The current of 4 mA represents a value of zero for the measured variable, but is useful since loss of current indicates a broken loop.

Refer to the signal transmitter in the later chapter "Hardware Building Blocks" for circuit detail.

Filtering

In many applications, noise can be a problem, producing varying or spurious readings. For use as feedback in a control system, it is essential that the possible frequency range of the signal is considered, and the effect of noise on the system output. For operator display purposes, an update rate of 2 to 4 times per second is acceptable and readable.

Filtering may be added to reduce noise on the signal. The filter has an averaging effect and delivers an output which is the average value of the input, thereby ignoring spikes and unwanted frequencies. Filtering is essential in areas which are "electrically noisy" (eg close to motors, power cables, frequency generators, power supplies etc) in order to produce a clean reliable signal. For most applications, a low pass filter is required to remove noise from thyristor drives, lighting and power supplies.

Filters are classified according to their frequency response characteristics, and as shown in figure 6.4 are described as being "low pass", band pass" or "high pass" referring to the range of frequencies which can pass through. The gain of a filter is often expressed in dB, with reference to the rate of attenuation outside the pass range.

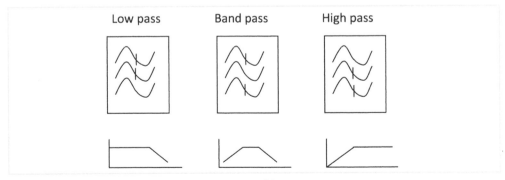

Figure 6.4 *Low pass, band pass & high pass filters*

Example

The most common form of low pass filter is the simple RC network, as shown in figure 6.5 (a), having a frequency response as shown in figure 6.5 (b). The cut-off frequency is set by the values of R and C. Being a first order lag, the attenuation of signals above the cut-off frequency is at a rate of 20 dB/decade.

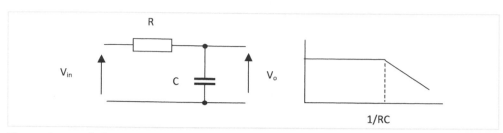

Figure 6.5 *a (left): RC filter; b (right): Filter frequency response*

Consider a filter with R = 1 kΩ and C = 1 μF, cut-off frequency = RC^{-1} = 1000 Radian/sec = 159 Hz. Figure 6.6 shows the filter gain at spot frequencies.

Frequency (Hz)	Gain
10	1
100	0,846
159	0,707
1590	0,1

Figure 6.6 *Gain versus Frequency for a Simple RC Filter*

Note that the gain is down to 0.707 at the cut-off frequency, and has fallen to 0.1 at ten times the cut-off frequency

The specification for this simple filter would therefore be,

Cut-off frequency	159 Hz
Phase shift at cut-off frequency	45 Degree
Attenuation	–20 dB/decade

This type of filter is simple, easily implemented, and effective in typical industrial applications where higher switching frequencies are to be eliminated. Note, however, that the signal frequency is a decade (10 times) higher before attenuation becomes significant.

A more sophisticated low pass filter is shown in figure 6.7, where an RC network forms part of the operational amplifier feedback path. The feedback of unwanted frequencies reduces the sensitivity to those frequencies. Note then, that a high pass network in the amplifier feedback path produces a low-pass filter amplifier response. Using a two-stage (second order) network in the feedback has the advantage that the filter has a sharper cut-off above the frequency range (–40 dB/decade).

In the circuit, R1 and C1 form a simple low pass filter, buffered by the amplifier. R2 and C3 form the amplifier feedback, hence setting the amplifier gain dependent upon their frequency characteristics. At higher frequencies, the impedance of C2 is low, thereby reducing the overall gain by higher feedback.

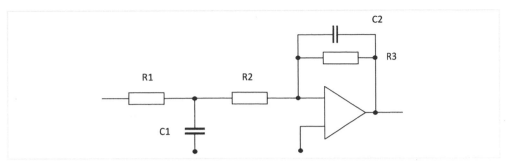

Figure 6.7   Second order low pass filter

Processing – Digital

Analogue to Digital converter

In processor based systems (ie systems using a PC, PIC, PAC or other microprocessor application), the analogue signal must be converted into a numeric value which can be stored in memory for later use by the programme. Typically:

⮕   for PC systems, a plug in card allows connection of multiple analogue channels, with selectable gain ranges;

⮕   for PIC systems, the converter is part of the chip and offers multiple input channels with a fixed input voltage range;

⮕   for PAC systems, an analogue input module may be fitted to the rack, typically with 4, 8 or 16 input channels, often selectable as voltage or current input.

There are several electronic techniques available to produce a binary value from an analogue input, the most desirable characteristics being speed and resolution. Typically, commercially available units offer 12 or 16 bit resolution, with conversion times of 10 microseconds per channel.

Most analogue inputs for processor based systems use a single channel converter preceded by a multiplexer, so that individual channels may be selected for conversion. This has the advantage that a single high performance converter may be used but has the drawbacks of extra software overhead and lower channel conversion rates. Further, the multiplexer samples the input signal to produce a steady voltage to the converter input, but the sample process also adds a time delay to the conversion. Figure 6.8 shows a typical analogue input system.

The input amplifiers have programmable gain, activated by logic levels which select a feedback resistor for each stage. In this manner, the input signal required to pro-

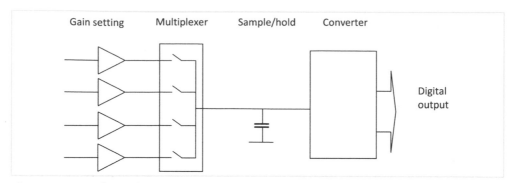

Figure 6.8   *Analogue input system*

duce the correct level into the converter may be set to suit the application. This is an essential step to ensure that maximum resolution is obtained for the available signal.

The multiplexer is also controlled by logic levels to select the current channel. This is normally accomplished under programme control to allow the user select the channel required. Typically, the programme would cycle around each channel in turn, so that every input channel is read in sequence. The values may be written into a table in memory for later access.

The capacitor at the output of the multiplexer is to acquire (sample) the selected channel for presentation into the converter, so that a steady signal is held at the input to the converter throughout the conversion process.

The converter is also controllable, typically having a "start" control input and a "conversion complete" output signal.

Software functions required are therefore,

➡   Set channel range

➡   Repeat
       Select input channel (multiplexer)
       Wait for sample time
       Start converter
       Wait for "conversion complete"
       Read digital value

Filtering and averaging

Once the input signal has been converted, it can be read and used in a programme. It is often desirable to apply filtering to the data for various reasons:

➠   the analogue signal may be noisy;

➠   the measured variable may have inherent noise (eg surface waves in liquid level);

➠   a longer term trend may be desirable;

➠   etc.

Since the conversion process is rapid, it will often be the case that high frequency noise on the signal may also be captured and converted, producing an erroneous result. Assuming that appropriate analogue filtering has been applied at the converter input to minimise such noise, digital filtering may be used to further process the data.

> An important analogue filter at the input to the converter is called an "anti-alias" filter. This prevents the input signal from being erroneously converted – see further reading.

Two examples of digital filtering are presented here, both easily programmed and effective:

➠   an error summing filter;
➠   a "moving average" filter.

Error summing filter

As its name suggests, the error summing filter operates in closed loop fashion by determination of the error between its output and input values, and using that error to correct the output value. For an input value X, and an output value Y, using a "filter weight" of k, we have

$$Y = Y + \frac{(X - Y)}{k}$$

This filter behaves with integral action, since the output value is retained, but "steered" in the direction of the next input value. In this manner, the output of the filter will ramp towards the input value, preventing rapid changes. The algorithm for this filter is

➠   Repeat
             Determine error between output and input
             Take a fraction of that error
             Add that error fraction to the current output

Consider this filter with a unit step input applied at $t = 0$, using a filter weight of 0.5. Applying the above algorithm, we can determine the output value, as shown in figure 6.9.

Time step	Input	Output	Error fraction
0	1	0	0.5
1	1	0.5	0.25
2	1	0.75	0.125
3	1	0.875	0.0625
4	1	0.9375	0.03125
5	1	0.96875	etc

Figure 6.9 *Filter output values*

The response approximates that of a first order lag. The "time constant" of the filter may be varied by adjustment of the error fraction, which effectively varies the number of samples required for the output to reach the input value. A large weight makes the filter output insensitive to changes in the input.

Moving average filter

This type of filter takes an average of the latest sample and a defined number of previous data values. Consider a signal sampled to produce a data value X_n, where n is the sample number, we determine the output Y,

$$Y = \sum_{0}^{n} X_n$$

For large values of n, the output Y is unresponsive to input change, being heavily weighted by past data. Smaller values of n result in a faster update and greater sensitivity to input change.

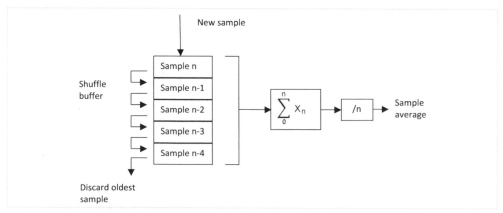

Figure 6.10 *Moving Average Filter*

The algorithm for this filter is

⟼   Repeat
        Read next data value
        Sum previous n values
        Divide sum by n

This is shown diagrammatically in figure 6.10, where samples are read into a buffer. The buffer contents are shifted by one position each time a new sample is taken, and the buffer average determined.

Data Transmission

For some applications, data will require transmission, in which case, consideration should be given to:

⟼   transmission distance;

⟼   noise effects;

⟼   use of analogue or digital signal;

⟼   error checking required.

For analogue signals, a current loop is preferred, since the input impedance at the receiver is low (typically 250 Ohms, producing a signal level of 1 – 5 Volts). This is better than using a 0 – 10 Volt signal, which would require much higher input impedance at the receiver to avoid potential divider attenuation effects, thereby making it susceptible to induced noise. (A length of cable at the input of a high input impedance amplifier makes an excellent radio receiver (!), and high frequency noise on the desired signal can produce undesirable effects). Transmission distances of 1 km or more are achievable using current loops, even in electrically noisy environments.

Digital data transmission is preferred where possible, since signal levels are essentially 0 or 1 and may therefore be more easily amplified and less susceptible to interference. Some instruments use RS232 or RS485 data transmission, but measurement sampling rate is limited by the speed at which data can be transmitted. Many instruments are available with in-built digital interface to facilitate longer distance or remote use (eg in process plant).

A common digital interface is the SSI (Serial Synchronous Interface) which many sensors and instruments support. Data is shifted out serially at high speed with reference to a clock waveform.

A popular alternative is the "bus system", where field devices are connected by common power supply and data cables. Each device has an address and communicates with a "bus master" for the purpose of high speed data transmission. The bus master interrogates devices in turn and produces raw data directly into the memory of the receiving device. Popular process industry examples are DeviceNet, Fieldbus and Profibus, whilst the Ethernet interface is becoming increasingly popular.

Data Display

Measured data can be presented to an operator in various ways, usually by means of a display or an HMI (Human-Machine Interface) screen. Ideally, the data will be displayed in meaningful (engineering) units after appropriate scaling of the input signal. Choice of readout depends very much upon operator preference or ease of interpretation (eg a bar graph as opposed to a seven segment type numerical display). A bar graph or trend may be easier to interpret at a glance, rather than by recognition of presented numerical information. Typically, an update rate of a numeric readout in the order of 1/3 second is satisfactory for the human eye to observe and appreciate, but a bar graph or other graphical type representation is much more readily assimilated, especially for observation of rising or falling trends.

Data logging

Data can be recorded for later viewing for purposes of quality control, consistency analysis, for observation of trends over a period of time or detection of maximum and minimum values. There are normally two scenarios where recorded data is of significance:

- in continuous processes, where one or more variables are of importance to the success of the process and quality of the product (eg furnace temperature in heat treatment or baking processes);

- in batch manufacturing processes where a sample of one or more critical variables may be taken as representative of the rest of the sample.

For the continuous process, a suitable sample rate should be chosen such that accuracy is not lost. A complete sample would include all required data and is referred to as a "data record". Such a record might appear as

```
Sample 1   Date, Time, Variable 1, Variable 2, Variable 3, Variable 4, etc...
Sample 2   Date, Time, Variable 1, Variable 2, Variable 3, Variable 4, etc...
Sample 3   Date, Time, Variable 1, Variable 2, Variable 3, Variable 4, etc...
etc.
```

a new record being created and appended to the file at the sample interval. It should then be possible to view the conditions under which the process was operating by production of a graph of all recorded variables. Data recorded from a continuous process may be used for a variety of reporting, quality control or inventory purposes, as well as being available for use within the real time control system (since the process is currently operating and the data has direct significance to that process output).

For the batch process, the sampling method is slightly different, in that the process may have completed, so the data taken cannot have any direct bearing upon the product, and is therefore applicable only for retrospective use (ie to correct process parameters for the next batch or as quality control and reporting information). Examples of batch processes are:

➡ bakery or heat treatment operations, where the quality of the product is checked after the process (in this case the oven temperature and time would be of interest, but only for correction to improve the next batch);

➡ acid bath or etching processes, where solution strength and immersion time are process parameters;

➡ mixing process, where quantity of each constituent is controlled.

Sampling from a batch requires identification of critical parameters of the finished product ("Key Process Indicators"), and the measurement of those parameters on a selected sample of the produced batch. Such measurement and analysis is usually presented statistically to observe trends in critical parameters, and is referred to as "Statistical Process Control".

SCADA

In many process applications, control is often distributed among hardware from different manufacturers. A SCADA (Supervisory Control and Data Acquisition) system is useful to enable control room monitoring of an entire process and to enable alarm functions, logging and management reporting. In order to enable connectivity between systems, a common hardware specification and software protocol is required, so that "data enabled" devices may be interrogated by the supervisory system. Most manufacturing or process industries will have this requirement, for example:

| Mining | Coal cutter, roof support, discharge and transfer systems, atmosphere monitoring etc., all having dedicated local control systems but requiring to be monitored and controlled from the surface |

Offshore	Drilling, pumping, storage and distribution
Chemical	Stock, feed, process control, discharge
Metals	Foundry, melting, casting, forming
Marine	Propulsion, guidance
Water	Reservoir and river levels, discharge rates, consumption, waste management

Traditionally, this requirement has been met by RS232 or RS485 serial data communication, using a "Master/Slave" software communication protocol such as Modbus. The RS232 / RS485 specification defines the hardware, whilst the communication protocol defines how data will be transferred.

Ethernet technology has developed and been adopted by the control engineering community in more recent years, since it allows direct connectivity into network and database systems using readily available hardware. Similarly, the Ethernet specification defines the hardware, using CAT5 or CAT6 cable for transfer speeds up to 100Mb/s or 1 Gb/s. In particular, the internet has driven this transfer to Ethernet technology, since data may be transferred and viewed worldwide.

Figure 6.11 shows how a simple Master / Slave system operates. The figure shows devices connected by an RS485 serial link. There is one bus master, (usually the SCADA system) and each connected slave device has a network address to allow recognition of message requests. In order to read data from a slave device, the master transmits a message containing the address of the unit to be queried and a command to request data read. The slave device, upon recognising the address portion, responds by processing the request and returning the requested data.

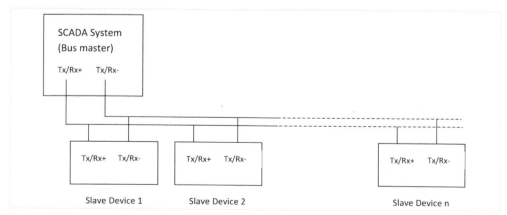

Figure 6.11   RS485 Master / Slave System

Example

A SCADA system is connected using an RS485 transmission loop to several slave devices. It is desired to read data held in the slave devices at regular intervals in order to provide readout to the operator and data storage. The system supports the Modbus protocol, and each device has been set a system address.

In the programme loop, the SCADA system polls each slave device to request the required data. Using the Modbus protocol, the Master sends the following serial message to read 8 registers from the device at address 1

```
Byte 0    Address                          01
Byte 1    Function code read register      03
Byte 2    Hi byte register address         00
Byte 3    Lo byte register address         01
Byte 4    Number of registers to read hi   00
Byte 5    Number of registers to read lo   08
Byte 6    CRC lo byte
Byte 7    CRC hi byte
```

Function code 3 is a standard Modbus command to read registers, the start address of those registers and the number of registers to read being specified in the following bytes. A checksum is added to the end of the message (Cyclic Redundancy Check) so that the receiver can create the same checksum independently, and verify that the received message is valid before acting upon that message.

The slave device replies

```
Byte 0    Address of replying unit          01
Byte 1    Function code read register       03
Byte 2    Number of data bytes to follow    10
Byte 3    Data hi byte                      xx
Byte 4    Data lo byte                      xx
Byte n    CRC lo byte
Byte n+1  CRC hi byte
```

The third message byte specifies how many data bytes follow, so that the entire message can be received. In this example, 16 data bytes follow (10 Hex). The CRC is again calculated at the receiver from the received characters, and should agree with that sent by the transmitter to prove data integrity. If an error is detected, the received data is ignored and only updated when the next correct message is received.

Human Machine Interface Packages

The Human Machine Interface (HMI) is the central point at which an operator views and controls a process. Many software packages are available which provide desired HMI features, having "drivers" for many controller and PAC types from different manufacturers.

A typical HMI package has a "configuration" mode for creation of the user interface display pages, and a "runtime" mode for operation (see also the later chapter "Programming for Control").

A typical HMI would include features of direct relevance to the control room operator, such as:

➠ mimic page display of individual processes or process parts;

➠ real time trending and graphical displays;

➠ storage of data to local computer disc or networked drive;

➠ alarm generation, operator alert and recording;

➠ ability to Start / Stop a particular process or change operating parameters.

Additional features might include

➠ "Recipe" or "Route Card" creation and recall to ensure process consistency;

➠ data warehouse and data mining features;

➠ web reporting, email alert etc.

Such packages rely upon the maintenance of a "tag database". A "tag" is a single piece of data which is read or written from / to the attached controller, and might be for example, a switch state, analogue value of a physical variable or other process parameter. Each tag will be used at some point in the HMI to convey its information appropriately to the operator.

By grouping together all tags from a particular controller hardware item, the "driver" for that specific controller is selected at the configuration stage as the means of data transfer to / from that tag. The driver will include specification as to how the data is transferred to the selected controller, including the protocol and refresh rate. Data transfer will take place in the Master / Slave scenario described above.

In this manner, a single HMI package can access data in several controllers using a different data communication specification for each. Common standards have been produced for such data transfer between different hardware from different manufacturers. In addition to the Modbus protocol described above (which was originally designed for RS485 serial systems, and has now been upgraded for Ethernet application as Modbus/TCP), other data transfer methodologies and standards have developed. "Dynamic Data Exchange" (DDE) was originally developed as a PC technology for real time data transfer between applications (on the same PC). Later improvement allowed access across networked computers by specification of three labels as an "address" to identify a particular tag within a particular computer application,

```
<Computer name>, <Application Name>, <Tag Name>
```

By reference to the three labels, any process on any computer could dynamically access any other tag on the same or any other connected (networked) computer. An improved specification was later developed (OPC) to provide the same mechanism with a more complete definition, and to be non vendor-specific.

OPC ("OLE for Process Control" (*Object Linking & Embedding for Process Control*)) is a standard developed by an automation industry task force in 1996, and since maintained by The OPC Foundation. The aim of OPC is to provide a bridge between different hardware and software applications using a common real-time data exchange format.

A common scenario within plant control systems is to allow multiple HMI screens, usually with different levels of access. The operator has appropriate screens for plant control, while other strategically sited screens are useful for plant diagnostics by maintenance personnel during plant operation. To reduce the communication loading on the connected controllers by the multiple HMIs, a "tag server" package runs on one of the HMIs to handle all communication with the controllers, and then to present those tags as requested by the other HMIs. The other HMI screens access the server rather than the controller, as shown in figure 6.12. In this manner, duplicity of data requests from the HMIs to the controller is avoided, allowing the controller to perform its real time operations without undue overhead.

Note that the HMI server would be handling multiple communications simultaneously with connected controllers, instruments and other HMI, probably with different protocols.

Data refresh rate is a concern where multiple controllers are accessed by a single HMI, since the communication speed is limited by the chosen standard (bit rates up to 115 kilo-baud for asynchronous serial data) ie the channel has limited "bandwidth". Ethernet technology with transmission rates up to 1 Gb/sec is preferred,

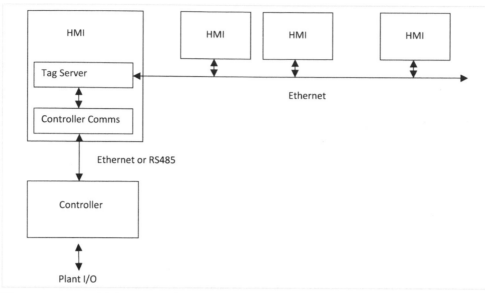

Figure 6.12   *Multiple HMI with Tag Server*

where a fibre "backbone" across the plant is useful, with cable connection into connected devices.

Whilst HMI packages offer a wide range of operator features and have powerful data reporting capability, they are usually priced according to the number of runtime tags – ie cost will be proportional to the complexity of the monitored process.

Summary

This chapter has presented the instrumentation system for measurement of physical variables, followed by appropriate processing, transmission, display and storage. It has listed sensor types, described common signal processing requirements, and has considered data logging for continuous and batch applications.

The chapter has also considered large scale applications where HMI packages collect data from several sources for operator information, reporting and control.

7
PIC n PAC

Choice of hardware

This chapter is concerned with the choice of computer hardware for control engineering applications. Whilst an off-the-shelf solution may be desirable, the control engineer is usually faced with a set of decisions based upon several factors, including:

⟶ system complexity;

⟶ I/O point count;

⟶ operator interaction techniques;

⟶ ease of programming, faultfinding and maintenance;

⟶ quantity required;

⟶ cost and size constraints.

Consider examples at opposite ends of the scale –

⟶ a washing machine controller, which has a small I/O count, simple computational requirements and little operator input. It is intended for a mass market, so therefore must be simple, small and low cost. Easy maintenance is not essential, since the entire unit will be replaced in the event of a fault;.

⟶ a large scale process plant, (refinery, steel mill, process plant etc) where only one such item exists, but will be comprised of many automated sub-processes, will have a high I/O count and high requirements for operator interaction. Cost is not such an important factor, since the system will be upgraded and evolve over a period of time as improvements are made, but ease of programming and maintenance will be essential to allow such modifica-

tion during continuous operation in a production or manufacturing environment.

Choice of hardware will often reduce to a selection from several possible solutions,
including:

⇒   off-the-shelf controller;

⇒   embedded programmable integrated circuit;

⇒   programmable controller (PLC or PAC);

⇒   PC.

Off-the-shelf controller

An off-the-shelf controller is an item which can be obtained easily (literally "off-the
shelf"), since it provides a simple closed loop control function which can be set up
to suit the application. Such controllers offer a wide range of input and output
types, often with plug-in board options to enhance functionality (eg communications, analogue output, alarm relay outputs) and are supplied in standard sized
equipment housing. These devices are usually configurable, in that internal parameters can be set to customise the unit to the application, for example:

⇒   source of set-point (front panel, analogue input or serial communications);

⇒   feedback device (thermocouple type, voltage, current etc);

⇒   alarm levels;

⇒   system tuning (PID control).

A simple example is a servo-amplifier intended for fractional-horsepower motors or
electro-hydraulic servo-valve control. These are typically purely analogue electronics, with preset potentiometer adjustment of offset, gain and loop parameters.

A more complex example is a furnace controller, supplied as panel-mounting instrument, providing operator input and display of the controlled temperature. The
unit will have inputs for a variety of temperature sensing devices (eg thermocouple,
RTD etc) to allow universal application across a range of processes and industries.
Setup is by means of front panel keys and display, with configuration stored to internal memory. Such a device will typically contain a dedicated microprocessor system with appropriate I/O.

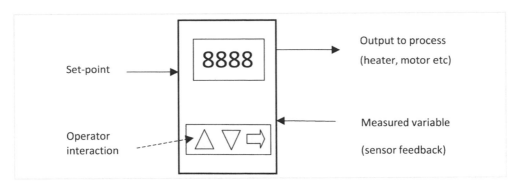

Figure 7.1   *Off-the-shelf controller application*

For the user, a simple controller is most advantageous, since the device is a propri-etary item built on proven technology, has multiple applications with support else-where, and requires minimum development time. Figure 7.1 shows application of an off-the-shelf controller.

Embedded programmable integrated circuit

Microprocessor chip technology has advanced significantly to the point where 64 bit processors are fabricated on the same chip as common I/O features (digital and analogue I/O, serial data communications etc). Flash type memory (ROM) is in-cluded along with on-board RAM, to produce a single chip computer, commonly re-ferred to as PIC (Programmable Interface Chip). Such devices have countless applications wherever embedded computing power is required, from domestic ap-pliances, audio-visual goods and off-the-shelf controllers to automotive and aero-space control applications.

Although initial software development costs may be high, the hardware is very cheap and the volume of sales is sufficient to recoup the investment.

Typically programmed in Assembly language or C, they remain firmly in the domain of the engineer sufficiently familiar with hardware and software techniques (as op-posed to some controllers we shall look at later). The advantages of such a device from a control point of view are significant:

➠   direct access to I/O hardware via memory;

➠   fast processing time (typically one microsecond per instruction);

➠   low chip count.

In a later chapter we shall look at programming techniques for this type of device, with control engineering applications.

Programmable controllers

The PLC

In industrial and process applications, hard-wired relay panels were almost always used for control, until the advent of logic systems and the microprocessor. The PLC (*Programmable Logic Controller*) was developed to provide a universal control engine, initially as a replacement for relay panels. Programmability meant that system function changes were easily accomplished in software, rather than by rewire of a relay system. The use of "ladder logic" as a programming tool meant that the PLC could be understood by factory electrician and engineer alike, without knowledge of traditional computer programming languages.

An example of a motor Start-Stop control in ladder logic programming is shown in figure 7.2. The "Start" pushbutton energises the output coil "Y1", and a contact on relay Y1 closes to latch the relay in the "On" state. Depression of the "Stop" pushbutton de-energises the relay and the latch is lost.

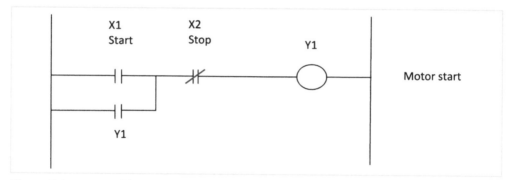

Figure 7.2 *PLC Ladder Logic Motor Starter*

The "programme" diagram is intended to look exactly the same as a relay circuit diagram, making it understandable by those more familiar with older hardware. By convention:

➠   the vertical lines represent the power supply;

➠   inputs are shown in the path starting at the left hand supply rail, with "signal flow" towards the right;

➠   outputs are always shown to the right hand side as a relay coil.

Most PLC's included timers and counters identical to the equivalent relay function. This style of programming was a tremendous step forward in logic control technology. As the PLC developed, analogue I/O and data communications were added, making the PLC a powerful controller and the first choice for many control solutions. Most were available as self-contained units with a mix of I/O, but also as rack-based systems where I/O modules could be inserted to suit the application. A further development was to add communications between racks, so that "remote I/O" could be accessed, ie a rack of I/O modules mounted away from the main processor, local to the plant I/O, forming a "distributed system".

The typical PLC includes diagnostics to allow rapid faultfinding, in that a rung can be viewed while the programme is running. Contacts in the circuit are highlighted to show if they are "made up" providing "power flow" to the rung output coil.

Whilst ladder logic is simple, it is inherently limited, and becomes particularly clumsy for non-trivial logic, data manipulation, string handling, communications and maths. The "Structured Text" programming feature and the use of "function blocks" were added to many PLCs in an attempt to make it more accessible to other programmers, although it did not bring additional features to address any of the shortcomings. Figure 7.3 shows the same motor Start-Stop control in structured text.

```
LD      X1              Start
OR      Y1              Motor  run contact
AND     X2              Stop
OUT     Y1              Motor  starter
```

Figure 7.3 *PLC Structured Text Motor Starter*

In the example, The "Start" pushbutton at input X1 is loaded on the first line of the programme, and then logic "ORed" with Y1, the relay latch contact. These are then "ANDed" with input X2, the "Stop" pushbutton, before output to the relay coil output Y1 on the last programme line. Comments on the right hand side assist readability (a label is assigned to each I/O point, so that during programme entry, the appropriate label is displayed).

The PLC was quickly adopted, finding widespread use, and remained the chosen solution for a period of 30 years. During the late 1900's while computer hardware was developing at a particularly high rate, PLC systems retained the same programming language methods, therefore endearing themselves to a generation of users by providing continuity in understanding for plant control engineers and maintenance personnel.

The PAC

Several factors contributed to the fall in popularity of the PLC. Technical issues which were once a significant advantage became a hindrance:

➠ comparative clumsiness of (ladder) programming;

➠ limited I/O speed (serial data bus);

➠ connectivity to other plant controllers, HMI and reporting systems;

➠ younger engineers not familiar with relay logic, but more acquainted with high level languages.

Other issues driven by the market and users, demanded a more sophisticated controller:

➠ data handling, trending and reporting;

➠ Ethernet connectivity;

➠ internet growth;

➠ ability to communicate with multiple mixed protocols simultaneously.

The *Programmable Automation Controller* (PAC) was a logical development of the PLC, but broke free from many of the constraints.

The first major step was the use of Ethernet connectivity, making possible the use of factory-wide systems, internet access to remote I/O and web reporting. Whilst network and database technology had been developing, the PLC had remained quite separate. By using Ethernet connectivity, it became possible to access I/O and data from a much wider field, at significantly higher speed, using relatively cheap, proven hardware. Many factories and process plant already had a network in place, so the "backbone" of communication was already in place, effectively bringing plant data and control to the desktop.

The second step was to abandon support for ladder style programming in favour of more modern structured languages. Ladder logic had served a useful purpose in the transition from hard-wired relay panel to computer-controlled system, and will remain in use for years to come, but is essentially of little use when compared to current methods.

The PAC provides far more features, many of these enabled by the use of Ethernet connectivity and different programme approach, which the PLC could never have achieved with its inherited constraints.

Typically, the PAC incorporates desirable features from established plant control technologies, including the PLC, RTU (*Remote Telemetry Unit*), distributed control system and PC. Supported by more common language styles, the PAC typically includes more advanced programming features such as

➠   data structures, with advanced indexing and addressing modes;

➠   multiple simultaneous communication protocols (serial, TCP, SSI, etc);

➠   file read/write, storage and transfer;

➠   email and data streaming;

➠   multiple HMI support

➠   etc;

in addition to the normal digital and analogue I/O.

The PC

The PC is often overlooked as being a means of control, usually due to impracticalities for use in a manufactured "catalogue" product and constraints on I/O connectivity. However, for use in testing, laboratory or research and development applications, the PC offers real advantages. The standard backplane of the PC bus led to the development of interface cards (ISA, MCI) which could be memory mapped and operated using proprietary driver software or with direct programme control. The development of the USB (Universal Serial Bus) led to further simple (external) interfacing.

The advantages of using a PC for control are:

➠   the range of languages available (Basic, C, Delphi, assembler);

➠   connectivity (it is relatively easy to add Ethernet and serial ports);

➠   data storage to built-in disc;

➠   software support (wide range of HMI, data analysis, graphing, web and development tools).

The major drawbacks of using a PC are:

➠   the practical limit to the number of I/O points which could be added;

➠   the difficulty in packaging it into a rugged unit suitable for industrial use.

Processing Speed

It is difficult to compare different processing speeds, and such comparison can be misleading in choice of a suitable control technique for a given application. A manufacturer will quote processing speeds for particular products, typically,

PIC	1 microsecond per instruction
PLC / PAC	500 microsecond per 1000 programme instructions

However:

➠ a PIC programmed in assembly language will require several hundred lines of code to perform any useful control task, or may be programmed in a high level language;

➠ a PLC will perform as stated, and response times may be more easily determined;

➠ PAC performance depends on many other factors (not just instruction execution time) given the additional included functionality.

It must be remembered that the processing speed is not such a major factor in choice of controller, as much as the response time of the process itself and the speed at which I/O may be updated. Eg:

➠ a furnace temperature control system. Temperature is typically slowly-varying, depending upon the thermal mass and insulating properties of the enclosure. An update rate of once per second or every ten seconds may be sufficient;

➠ a motor speed control system. Motor speed depends upon applied torque and the load properties. An analogue electronic control loop will provide fast response, but a digital position or speed control system might require a sample rate of one per millisecond to achieve suitable positioning response;

➠ a pressure control system for pipe or pressure-vessel testing. Pressure in a closed vessel will rise very quickly, depending upon the rate of fluid input. An update rate of once per millisecond or faster would be appropriate.

Interfacing

For the PIC or PAC to have any useful function, it must be interfaced to "real world" signals, having standard voltage levels (eg 24 V or 110 V for digital I/O, 0 – 10 V or

4 – 20 mA for analogue I/O). Microprocessor chips have a supply of 5 volts dc and therefore recognise anything below 1 volt as a logic "0", and above 2.5 volts as a logic "1". Similarly, on-chip analogue inputs will be constrained to the 0-5 volt range.

For PIC or PAC systems, the interface requirements are the same, except that the packaging will be different. PIC systems will have the interface circuitry on-board, whilst a PAC system will have separate I/O modules in a typical rack mount plug-in format.

Digital Inputs

Figure 7.4 shows a digital input interface. The optical coupler provides electrical isolation between the plant supply and the processor supply. The LED provides visual indication that the input is on or off. Input resistor R sets the current through the coupler. For a current of 5mA sufficient to illuminate the LEDs, and assuming a 1 volt drop across each LED, the resistor is selected depending upon the input voltage.

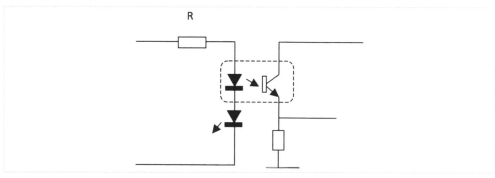

Figure 7.4   *Isolated digital input*

For 24V inputs,

$$R = \frac{24 - 2}{0.005}$$

Ie R = 4.4 kohms, (typically 4.7 k).

For 5V inputs,

$$R = \frac{5 - 2}{0.005}$$

Ie R = 600 ohms.

Digital outputs

It is usually desirable to switch dc or ac output signals for industrial control purposes. Figure 7.5 shows a dc output interface, with optical isolation between plant supply and processor supply.

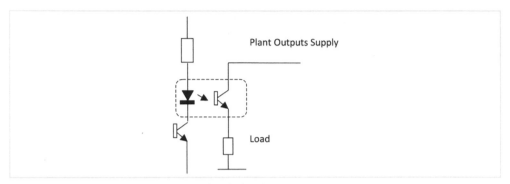

Figure 7.5   *Isolated digital output for dc load*

Figure 7.6 shows an ac output interface also with supply isolation. A feature of ac output interfaces is to provide "zero voltage switching", such that the output device turns on when the supply is close to zero volts in the ac cycle, to reduce the effect of noise spikes which would be generated if the device were to turn on later in the cycle. The switching device is a triac, conducting in both directions when a trigger signal is applied to the gate terminal.

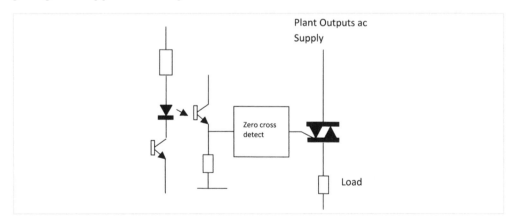

Figure 7.6   *Isolated digital output for ac load*

Analogue inputs

There are several methods of operation for analogue to digital converters, often with trade-off between speed and resolution. In typical systems, a 12 or 16 bit result is typical, with conversion times of 10 to 100 micro-second.

If the output is a 12 bit number, the smallest change in the input which can be detected is one part in 2^{12}, ie 1 part in 4096, or 0.024%. This smallest change is called the "resolution", representing the "weight" or value of the least significant bit.

For 16 bit systems, the resolution is improved to one part in 65536, or 0.00015%. Typically the result would appear as a signed integer, with the range -32768 to $+32768$.

Analogue outputs

Figure 7.7 shows an analogue output interface with a simple "weighted resistor" digital to analogue converter. The resistor values are chosen to set the amplifier gain appropriately according to the "weight" of the input bit.

Consider a 12 bit converter, with amplifier feedback resistor of 10 k, input voltage 5 V and an output voltage of $0 - 10$ V.

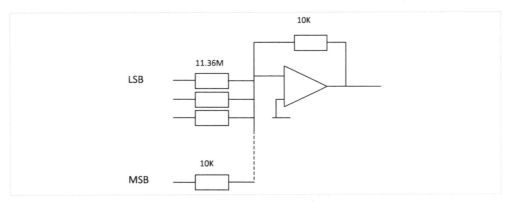

Figure 7.7   *Weighted resistor D-A converter*

For the least significant bit,

$$V_o = \frac{10}{2^{12}} = 2.44 \text{ mV} \quad \text{and} \quad \text{amplifier gain} = \frac{0.00244}{5} = 0.000488$$

$$\text{so } R_{12} = \frac{10000}{0.000488} = 11.36 \text{ M}$$

For the most significant bit,

$$V_o = \frac{10}{2^1} = 5 \text{ V} \quad \text{and} \quad \text{amplifier gain} = \frac{5}{5} = 1$$

$$\text{so } R_1 = \frac{10000}{1} = 10 \text{ k}$$

The other resistor values may be determined in the same way. Normally, these resistors would be fabricated on the chip during manufacture with precision values.

Serial I/O

Serial data communications are widely employed for interfacing purposes. In particular, barcode readers, scanners, weigh scales, remote alpha-numeric displays and modems all rely on serial transmissionof data. Serial communication is useful where data is to be transferred over long distances, between computers, or simply to make a convenient 2-wire interface.

Communication may be one-way (eg a computer sending data to a remote display) or two-way (eg a computer requesting data from a remote device, which then responds). Standards exist to which manufacturers and users conform, the most common being RS232 and RS485.

Transmitter

Data is transmitted one bit at a time at a fixed rate. This is achieved by transferring one byte (character) at a time into a shift register, then shifting all bits by a clock input, as shown in figure 7.8. The bits shifted out form the serial data stream for transmission. The clock frequency fixes the bit-rate (referred to as Baud rate), while the rate at which charaters are transferred is known as the character rate.

Most commonly, transfer is asynchronous, in that the character rate is not fixed, the next character being transmitted when the transmitter and receiver are both ready (usually tested in software). Data can be transferred synchronously using a

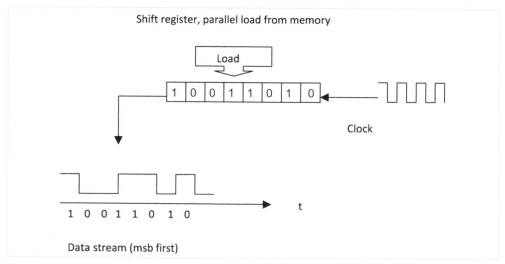

Figure 7.8   Serial Data Transmitter

fixed clock resulting in a faster memory-to-memory transfer, but its use is ʀ nearly so widespread.

Receiver

The receiver must accept the incoming bit stream and perform the reverse of th transmit operation. The bits are received into a shift register, and shifted along at each bit interval, as shown in figure 7.9. After all bits have shifted in, the register will hold the original transmitted byte, ready for transfer into receiver memory.

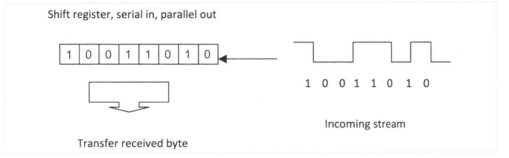

Figure 7.9   Serial Data Receiver

The receiver must detect the arrival of the first bit in order to transfer the successive bits into the correct place within the byte. This is achieved by encapsulating the serial data into a "transmission frame", consisting of a "Start bit" and a "Stop bit" of fixed length, in order that the receiver clock system may synchronise with the incoming stream as shown in figure 7.10. Errors are caused when the receiver does not properly detect the bits and save them into the correct place in the byte. This is called a "framing error" or "overrun error".

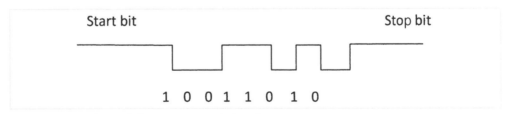

Figure 7.10   The Serial Data Transmission Frame

Hardware

The most common device used for serial communication is the Universal Asynchronous Receiver Transmitter (UART). The UART contains all the clock generation and shift register hardware required to form the transmitter and receiver. As a single chip, the UART will have a parallel memory interface so that data bytes may be written to the transmitter and received bytes read back into memory. In PIC sysms, the UART appears a a functional block within the chip and is accessed easily through transmit and receive registers.

Most UARTs operate from the computer internal 5 volt supply and therefore produce a 5 volt output bit stream from the transmitter, and require a 5 volt level input stream to the receiver. UARTs may be conected directly, ie the transmitter output of one device connected to the receive input of the other, to facilitate two-way communication.

Serial transmission standards (such as RS232) define different voltage levels to allow interconnection of devices, so a driver chip is used to convert the voltage level of the output of the UART. The driver chip will also provide current limiting to protect against short circuit on the line.

Figure 7.11 shows an interface based on the MAX232 chip, which is ideal for such interfacing since it operates from a single 5 volt supply, but produces the required RS232 signal levels. The chip has an on-board voltage converter, producing the required +/- 12 volt supplies. Typically, the driver handles signal inversion, so that a "1" is actually transmitted as a negative voltage level.

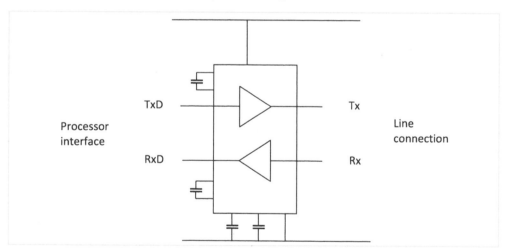

Figure 7.11   MAX232 Communication interface chip

Summary

This chapter has considered the use of available hardware for control applications, including dedicated controllers, the PIC, PLC, PAC and PC. It has considered the development of the popular PLC into the PAC, and has considered I/O interfacing for digital and analogue signals.

8
Programming for Control

Software for control engineering

For most control applications, a programmable solution will be chosen – a PIC, PLC or PAC as discussed in an earlier chapter. Software for these devices will be unique to the application, since each project or process has peculiar I/O and HMI requirements. It is useful to adhere to accepted practice in the production of software, since there are certain desirable features,

Readability	understandable by others
Maintainability	easily modified or upgraded
Portability	able to run the same strategy or functions on other hardware or in other languages (assuming minor modifications to suit)
Conformity	accepted protocols or conventions (eg communication protocols, standard data formats)

Software tools

The manner in which the programme is written depends upon the hardware chosen and the software tools which are available to support it. From the control engineer's viewpoint, choice will depend upon given project criteria, including:

➧ processing speed;

➧ ease of I/O access;

➧ HMI features;

➧ data storage;

⇒   communications;

⇒   application and environment.

This chapter considers the manner in which the different devices are programmed, then considers techniques available to the programmer to maximise response.

PLC Programming

Figure 8.1 shows the standard route to PLC programming.

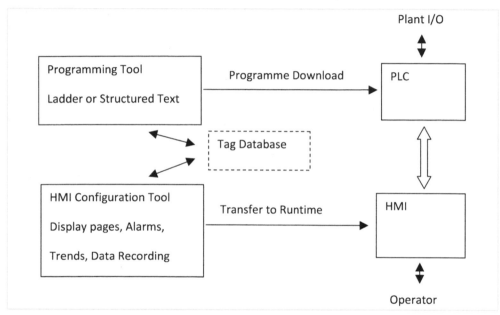

Figure 8.1   PLC Programming Tools

The "Programming Tool" allows creation of the ladder logic or structured text description of the control strategy. The tool generates the necessary code for the PLC, which is then downloaded to the PLC for execution. During programming, the "Tag Database" is created, containing a record of all connected I/O points and any internal variables used. "Tags" may be simply a digital I/O point, a timer, counter, integer, floating point number, character, string etc. The tag database therefore "personalises" the PLC to the actual process, by providing a description of all I/O point names and a "memory map" of all internal variables used during PLC programme execution.

A separate tool is used for HMI screen development, normally consisting of two parts,

➠   a "Configuration tool", this being similar to a CAD package allowing creation of graphic displays, operator input and display,

and

➠   a "Runtime" programme

The configuration tool is used to create all the required display pages. It requires access to the PLC programme tag database so that any item on a display page can be linked to a tag in the PLC programme. In this manner, the configuration tool provides text or value display, change of colour, movement and animation based upon the status or value of the tag (I/O points, internal variables, counters, timers etc). Useful displays are bar graphs and meters, which can be attached to a PLC tag to update as the value changes (eg liquid level in a tank etc).

The configuration package will also have the ability to include a real time graph or trend display, where a suitable time-base may be set and a PLC tag selected as the Y axis variable. Such a trend will also have the ability to record data to disc at a preset interval.

Alarms are also a feature of the configuration, where a PLC tag is linked to an alarm message, thus requiring operator attention when the selected tag changes state or its value goes outside a preset range.

Having used the configuration tool to create all required display pages, the "Runtime" programme is invoked to allow communication between the PLC and the HMI, so that the pages are updated dynamically.

SCADA packages

In larger plant control systems, it is useful to operate SCADA (*Supervisory Control And Data Acquisition*) systems as discussed in the Instrumentation chapter. The tag database may be made available for Read / Write by the SCADA system. The PLC HMI usually handles this function, since it is in communication with the PLC and can operate as a data server to requesting devices.

Debug tools

During programme development and later maintenance, it is useful to have a debug facility, where the PLC programme can be inspected during execution. The debug tool allows the user to observe connected I/O points as well as all internal tags. A useful feature in debugging is the ability to "force" inputs or outputs, so that a section of programme logic may be tested.

PIC Programming

Figure 8.2 shows the standard route to PIC programming.

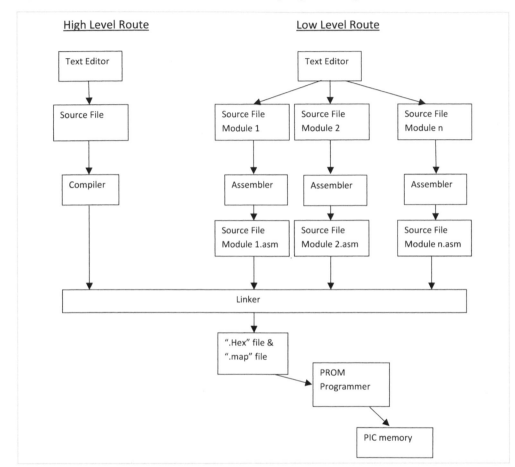

Figure 8.2 *PIC Programming Tools*

There are essentially two possible routes towards programming a PIC,

⇒ , a high level language, such as C (often called "embedded C"), or "flow-code"

or

⇒ assembly language

The high level language is usually preferred, and "C" has become increasingly popular for this device. Choice of a high level language also allows portability across different PICs in the same or other "family" of devices.

The low level route is chosen in the interests of speed or programme simplicity. Another major influence is the size of programme which can be contained in the PIC, since high level languages tend to produce larger files unless data types are carefully chosen.

Text Editor

A standard text editor is used to create files, the only criteria being that the syntax of the chosen language must be followed. The output from the editor is called a "source" file, since all other information generated to programme the PIC originates from this file.

Compiler

The compiler processes a high level language source code file to produce code which can be executed on the PIC device (machine code).

Assembler

The assembler processes the assembly language source code file to produce code which can be executed on the PIC device (machine code).

Typically, several modules will be required to make up the entire project. It is usual to maintain a library of modules, each having a specific function. For a particular application, the required functions are chosen and the appropriate modules selected.

Linker

A linker control file is used to specify which individual modules are to be combined into the PIC programme. The modules specified may be from a high level or low level language source. Each module is assigned a fixed address in the PIC programme memory area (flash ROM). Programme calls or jumps can then be resolved since the jump or call address has been assigned. Variables are also assigned a particular memory address within the PIC data area, so memory read/write addresses can then be allocated.

The Linker produces a single ".hex" file which is an image of the code to be loaded directly into the PIC memory, and a ".map" file, showing the memory locations of each code segment and variable.

PROM Programmer

PICs have on board programmable memory for long-term programme storage. This memory is usually termed "flash EPROM" since it is electrically programmed into the PIC. The PROM programmer has a socket into which the PIC is placed. Programming is usually by means of applying a programming voltage to one of the PIC pins, while scrolling through the addresses writing appropriate data. Once the programming is complete, the PIC is ready to be placed into its application circuit board.

Debug tools

Powerful debug tools are available for PIC devices, similar to those used for microprocessor systems. The most useful of these are

Simulator	a programme which runs on the development PC and simulates execution of the developed programme. Inputs can be changed to on or off and variables inspected. Single step features allow memory contents to be viewed after each instruction.
Emulator	a programme which runs on the development PC, but with a hardware connection to the target hardware system. The PC emulates the PIC chip, providing all the necessary I/O as present on the PIC. The emulator is significantly more useful than a simulator, since it operates on the target hardware.

PC Programming

Most interface cards for use with a PC are supplied with a software driver utility. The driver is a piece of software which allows the user to read / write the I/O device, whilst providing a simple interface to the application programme.

PC operating systems and their associated user interface have become very graphical, and access to hardware has been increasingly restricted. The operating system provider usually makes available an "application interface" by means of which programmes may access hardware devices (disk, keyboard, display etc). The software driver makes use of this interface to control the hardware.

For most PC users, it is desirable to access hardware directly from existing data handling, analysis or spreadsheet packages. The software driver provides the means of such transfer.

Figure 8.3 shows the standard route to PC programming. Application packages such as spreadsheets do allow real time connection to data through OPC links, but a high level language programming utility will offer greater flexibility.

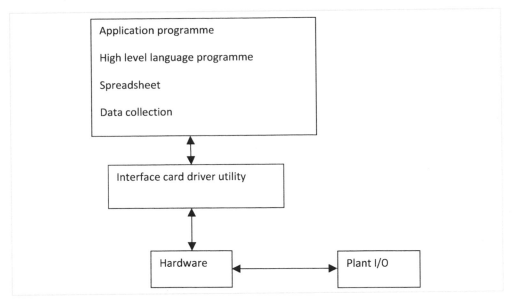

Figure 8.3   PC I/O Programming

Real time rules

Since we are controlling an output variable, there will always be a time-base to consider, which will govern the manner in which the programme should operate. For slowly varying systems, such as a furnace temperature control, speed of response may not be a particular consideration, since the programme will easily execute its tasks within the time the process undergoes an appreciable change. For faster systems, such as a robot motion control, a much more rapid response is required in order to achieve satisfactory accuracy.

Programme tasks

A programme or software module running on any computer system is referred to as a "task". In control applications, it is highly desirable that the system has real-time response and be capable of multi-tasking (ie able to run several tasks at the same time).

The simplest form of operating system is to have a task list, where all the programmes are stored in memory and executed one after another (termed "round robin" execution). In this manner, all tasks are executed sequentially, each having full access to all processor resources during its execution. The drawback of this method is that some tasks may be more consuming of time than others, and the time taken for a task to complete may not be consistent, depending upon the nature of its duties (operator requests, displays etc). It is therefore not possible for this method to be deterministic, ie to have reliable timing and consistent response.

An improvement to the task list approach is to apportion each task a time slice, driven by a regular clock, such that each task takes full control of the processor for the duration of its time slice. A supervisory task calls the next task upon the due time interval. Typically, a real-time operating system may allocate a 10 millisecond time slice to each task. When the task time is expired, control is relinquished to the supervisor, and the following task is allowed to continue. During each time slice, the processor continues from where it left off at the previous interval. When a task gives up its allocated time slice, the task status must be saved (ie programme counter, accumulators and any status registers) in order that programme execution can resume from where it left off.

This technique is frequently used in PLCs and PACs, where a set of instructions can be grouped into a chart or list, and executed at a predefined time interval.

Aside – Real Time computing, a historical note

The term "Real Time" is widely used but often misunderstood, being a legacy of early computer applications.

Early computers were programmed by punched cards or paper tape, which took time to prepare, and would be submitted to the computer to be run as a "batch" or "offline" application, requiring human intervention to run the programme. With limited I/O facilities, such programming relied upon operator entry and paper printout.

The term "real time" came into use with the concept of "Stored Programme" (ie the programme was stored in computer memory for rapid use, rather than by operator entry) and with the application of electronic I/O. It then became possible to obtain a more immediate response to external events, and "real time" became a sales feature. For a while, "real time" and "batch" applications were recognised as quite different disciplines, until the advent of personal computing as we recognise it today.

Interrupts

One of the most successful techniques to obtain real-time response in embedded control systems is the use of interrupts to create a "foreground / background" environment.

The interrupt handler is a useful part in a microprocessor system, the mechanism of operation being shown in figure 8.4. Interrupts are generated by an I/O event, such as a key-stroke, switch change-of-state, serial character received, mouse-click etc. Upon receipt of the interrupt, the processor is diverted to the Interrupt Service Routine (ISR). The present context is saved (programme position, status register etc), and execution continues at the service routine. At the end of that routine, a Return From Interrupt (RTI) instruction enables the processor to recover the stored context of the previously running programme, and continue where it left off.

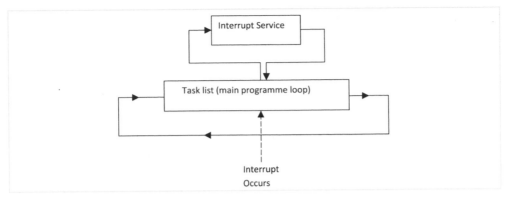

Figure 8.4   *The Interrupt mechanism*

For real time programming, a clock oscillator is used to interrupt at regular intervals (eg 1 or 10 milliseconds), and the ISR arranged to call all the time-critical tasks. This ensures that certain tasks receive regular attention, (foreground tasks) while less important tasks continue in sequence in the background. It is essential to check that the foreground tasks do not overrun by occupying too large a time portion, hence exceeding the interrupt period.

For control system purposes, the logic and system control tasks are placed in the foreground to ensure reliable fast response, while operator display, keyboard and other slower tasks are run in background. A later chapter presents sample code showing background task and interrupt service routines.

The art of programming

Having considered the technical requirements and tools available, it is worth reviewing established software engineering techniques with regard to actually writing a programme. The two main factors to consider are performance and readability – the programme should be able to carry out the intended task efficiently, and be sufficiently well structured and documented to make it easy to modify or upgrade later. For the purpose of this chapter, we consider a recognised means of programme development and illustrate how software may be documented.

Structured programming

A set of rules defines how we may write software to make it efficient and understandable by others. Expressed in simple terms:

⟶   use "top down" design to identify software requirements;

⟶   break down each task to lower levels, until a point is reached where code can be produced;

⇒   document using a "Structure Design Chart";

⇒   define each module function in structured text;

⇒   programmes should "flow through" to allow other modules their share of a
      time slice (ie do not hold the processor in an endless loop). Upon entry to the
      module, use a decision to determine what is to be done, perform that task,
      then exit;

⇒   each module should be no more than 20 – 30 lines long.

The following trivial example illustrates the principles of top-down design. Consider a liquid mixing process, where two liquids are admitted to a tank, mixed and
then poured, as shown in Figure 8.5.

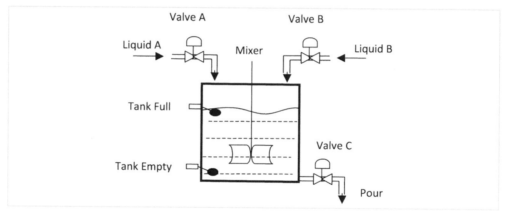

Figure 8.5   Liquid Mix Process

Figure 8.6 shows how top-down design produces a Structured Design Chart, arriv-
ing at a level of function description ready to start programming.

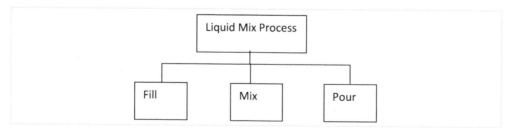

Figure 8.6   Structured Design Chart for Liquid Mix

Since the example is trivial, there is no point in describing the functions in further
detail, so the Structure Design Chart has only two levels. In a typical system, there
would be at least three levels depending upon the complexity of the project.

Having described the system to a point where the individual functions can be programmed in the desired language code, the next step is to produce a structured text description, (sometimes referred to as "pseudo-code", because it is not an actual language, but describes the functionality of the module in a form which can readily be coded in any programming language).

For the top level, we can write the structured text description

```
If Operator Start Request
    If Tank Empty, Request Fill
    If Fill Complete, Request Mix
    If Mix complete, Request Pour
End of process
```

Note that the top level will be supervisory, in that it is managing when the smaller make-up functions will operate. The lower level functions will contain more detail, relating to plant I/O. The Fill function may be similarly described in structured text

```
If Request Fill
    Close Valve C
    If Tank Empty, Open Valve A and Valve B
    If Tank Full, Close Valve A and Valve B
    Signal "Fill Complete"
End of Process
```

Having broken down the process and reached a level where individual I/O points are referenced, it is appropriate to start programming in the language tool for the chosen hardware solution.

The Concept of State

The structured text description is satisfactory for many applications and is readily converted into programme statements for any language. The above example shows how easily a task may be defined, but the use of the "If-Then-Else" construct, whilst appropriate in many circumstances, becomes clumsy to define more complex situations.

A "state" representation is often more appropriate for machine or process control where different operations are taking place. Essentially, a state is a condition or status of the process, having a defined entry into that state, and defined exit methods. Consider again the liquid mix application, the supervisory level and the tank fill may be described in state form.

Considering the supervisory (top) level, there are four recognisable states, shown in figure 8.7.

State	Operation	Exit Conditions
Idle	Nothing Happening	Operator Start request
Filling	Fill Valves Open	Tank Full
Mixing	Mixer On	Mix Complete
Pouring	Pour valve Open	Tank Empty

Figure 8.7 Process states

The figure shows how each state is described, and becomes a useful part of the software documentation.

In structured text, the "Case Structure" is used to describe the process states – a construct available in most programming languages. Only one state is active at any time, corresponding to a particular operation. During programme execution, the only activity in each state is to look for the exit condition, whereupon the next state will become active. The process top level states may be represented as shown in figure 8.8.

```
Switch (Process State)
    Case Idle
        If Operator Start Request
        Then Process State = Filling
    Break

    Case Filling
        If Fill Complete
        Then Process State = Mixing
    Break

    Case Mixing
        If Mix Complete
        Then Process State = Pouring
    Break

    Case Pouring
        If Tank Empty
        Then Process State = Idle
    Break
  End switch
```

Figure 8.8 Liquid mix top level

Software documentation

As with any engineering project, appropriate documentation is essential to ensure readability and maintenance. In particular, where multiple authors are involved, a common format should be used. Even in smaller, single author projects, it is useful to adhere to document conventions. Documentation will be different depending upon the project, the controlled plant or machine, processor type, programming language etc. Similarly, requirements will be different for high volume production or for a single, custom installation. Whatever the end product, different levels of the process should be defined, including:

Functional Specification	Complete text description of the process or plant to be controlled, defining all functions, operating modes, operator input and readout, data storage and transfer requirements, I/O list etc
Hardware architecture	Layout schematic showing processors, local and remote I/O stations, HMI terminals, signal connectivity, node addresses
Programming language	Tools used to create the programme, version, author and date
Structured Design Charts	"Top down" process definition
Module description	Text description of each module, including operation, input and output parameters
Symbol table	For each I/O point and for each internal memory, counter, timer or other tag, a description including the plant reference, a symbol for use in the programme text and a description of function
Version control	When modifications are made after initial issue, a record to be kept of changes made and for what reason
Comments	Some software is inherently self-documenting and recognisable, but useful higher-level comments should be added to programme code to aid readability during later inspection and upgrade

Summary

This chapter has considered software for control applications, including PLC, PIC and PC programming tools. It has also considered real time programming techniques and appropriate software design and documentation methods.

9
Hardware Building Blocks

This chapter presents a library of circuit designs for some of the most commonly used interfaces, processing circuits and controllers required by the control engineer. The circuits are intended for reference purposes and complete design analysis is not presented. The designs are grouped by function, presented in three sections of the chapter:

➠   instrumentation, feedback and signal processing;

➠   closed loop controllers;

➠   forward path drivers (actuator and final device control).

Instrumentation, feedback and signal processing

Signal transmitter

Figure 9.1 shows a signal transmitter, commonly used in the process industries for level conversion, transmission and re-transmission. The circuit is a closed loop system, setting current in the output load. This is particularly useful for signal conversion (0 – 10 V to 4 – 20 mA) or for transmission over long distances, since the closed loop compensates for varying load resistance.

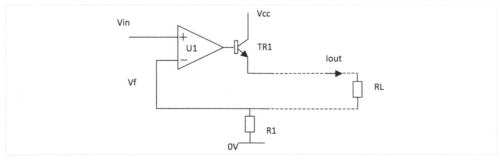

Figure 9.1 *Signal transmitter*

Current into the load resistance R_L is regulated by the series transistor TR1. The same current passes through R1, producing a feedback voltage V_f. The amplifier is considered to be of high gain, such that for practical purposes,

$$V_f = V_{in} \quad \text{and output current} \quad I_{out} = \frac{V_{in}}{R1}$$

The output current is controlled in closed loop since the differential amplifier U1 determines the error between V_{in} and V_f, and drives the transistor. For positive errors $(V_{in} > V_f)$, the amplifier output will be positive, turning on TR1 harder to pass increased current. For negative errors, $(V_{in} < V_f)$, the amplifier output will be negative, turning off TR1 to reduce the output current. Under steady state conditions, the amplifier output will be sufficient to maintain TR1 emitter, V_o, at

$$V_o = I_{out} \cdot (R_L + R1)$$

A minor drawback of this simple circuit is that the load resistance is not referenced to zero, since the lower end of the load is elevated by the voltage produced across R1. Whilst this is not a problem where two (non-earth) wires are used for the load (as opposed to a common return path with others in a typical plant installation), a preferred version is shown in figure 9.2. The sensing resistor R1 is placed in the "high side" of the output path, but a further amplifier is required to determine a feedback voltage proportional to output current.

For both versions of the circuit, maximum output current is limited to

$$I_{max} = \frac{V_{CC} - V_s}{R_L + R1}$$

where V_s is the saturation voltage of the transistor. V_{CC} and R1 should be chosen accordingly to give sufficient "headroom" for the desired output range.

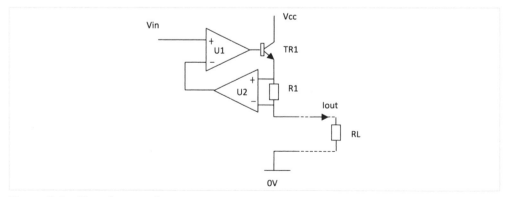

Figure 9.2 Signal transmitter

Instrumentation amplifier

Figure 9.3 shows the circuit of an instrumentation amplifier. The circuit is particularly useful where high gain is required, and has high input impedance. The circuit can be made from individual amplifiers, but are widely available as a single-package chip. Amplifier gain is set by resistor ratio. The individual amplifiers are considered infinite gain operational amplifiers.

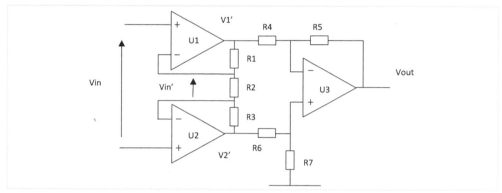

Figure 9.3 *Instrumentation amplifier*

For the first stage, U1 and U2, the output voltage is $(V1' - V2')$, becoming the input to the second (differential) amplifier, U3.

Since the amplifiers are high gain, the voltages at their inverting and non-inverting inputs will be the same, so we can write

$$V_{in}' = V_{in}$$

So for the output resistor network R1, R2 and R3,

$$\frac{V1' - V2'}{R1 + R2 + R3} = \frac{V_{in}}{R2}$$

R1 and R3 are equal, so the first stage gain is therefore

$$\frac{V1' - V2'}{V_{in}} = \frac{2R1 + R2}{R2}$$

or

$$\frac{V1' - V2'}{V_{in}} = 1 + \frac{2R1}{R2}$$

The overall gain of the amplifier is therefore

$$\frac{V_{\text{out}}}{V_{\text{in}}} = \left(1 + \frac{2R1}{R2}\right) \cdot \frac{R5}{R4}$$

Strain gauge amplifier

Strain gauges are used in a variety of applications, in particular for weighing, load cells and pressure measurement. Gauges are normally placed in a bridge arrangement to provide improved sensitivity and to compensate for temperature variation (rather than by simple potential divider). Output from the bridge is typically in the order of a few milli-volts, so a gain factor of somewhere between 100 and 1000 is typically required to produce a useful signal level.

Figure 9.4 shows a typical strain gauge amplifier, based upon the instrumentation amplifier previously described. Since the amplifier has particularly high input impedance and significant gain, shielding is required on the input cables. A zero function will also be required since an offset of only a few milli-volts at the input will produce a significant output.

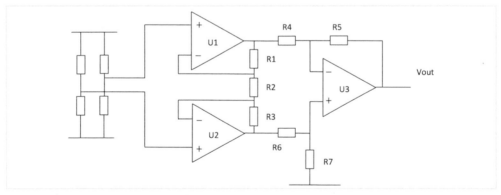

Figure 9.4   Strain gauge amplifier

Auto-zero

For some measurements, long-term drift or variation is a problem caused by other factors inherent to the process. A typical example is a weighing system based on strain gauges, where seasonal temperature variations create a false reading due to thermal expansion and contraction of the supporting or load-bearing members. The effect can be corrected by constantly driving the output to zero over a long time period (ie significantly longer than the measurement period so the effects of the correction are negligible). Figure 9.5 shows a hopper weighing system, where strain gauges on the legs measure compression, providing an output proportional to the weight of the contained substance.

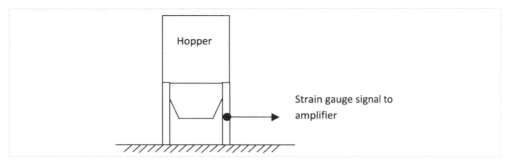

Figure 9.5   *Hopper strain gauge weighing system*

Figure 9.6 shows a signal amplifier based around U1, with gain R2/R1. The output of the amplifier is monitored by an integrator, based upon U2 with C1 and R5. If the output of the amplifier stage U1 is non-zero, the integrator output will ramp, at a rate set by the values of C1 and R5. The integrator output is applied to the signal amplifier input in opposite phase, such that the output will always be driven to zero.

Selection of the integrator time constant is important, such that comparatively rapid signals can pass through the amplifier, but long term variations are cancelled.

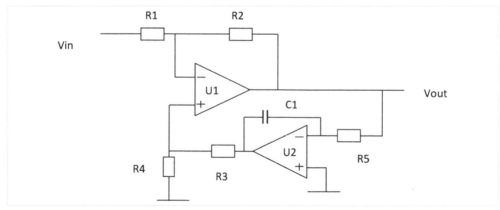

Figure 9.6   *Auto-zero amplifier*

Peak detect

It is often useful to capture the peak value of a signal. Figure 9.7 shows a fast peak detector. Input amplifier U1 forms a buffer, with feedback from the output voltage, V_{out}. For the case ($V_{in} > V_{out}$), amplifier U1 output will be positive, thereby charging C1 through diode D1. For the case ($V_{in} < V_{out}$), the amplifier U1 output will be negative, so C1 will remain at whatever voltage is stored after the last charge cycle. Amplifier U2 is a high impedance input to minimise C1 discharge, and present the stored peak at its output.

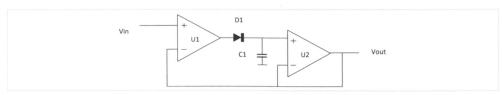

Figure 9.7 *Peak Detect*

To reset the peak hold, a discharge path for C1 is required.

Closed loop controllers

DC Servo-amplifier

Figure 9.8 shows the circuit of a differential amplifier, based upon a standard operational amplifier. This circuit forms the heart of closed loop control systems, since

$$V_{\text{out}} = \left(\frac{R4}{R2}\right) \cdot (V_{\text{in}(+)} - V_{\text{in}(-)})$$

The circuit has gain and zero adjustment by means of R4 and R7 respectively, producing a general purpose servo-amplifier. An output driver stage may be added to produce sufficient current for small motors or hydraulic servo-valves for automation applications. For current controlled actuators, a current setting output stage as shown in figure 9.2 above is desirable, since current will be set correctly under changing temperature (and hence resistance) conditions.

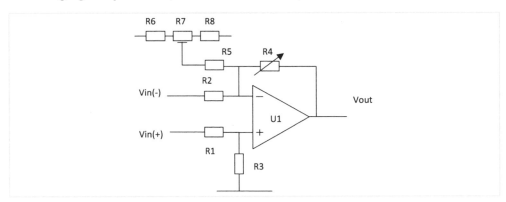

Figure 9.8 *DC Servo-amplifier*

3 term controller

Analogue electronic controllers have largely been superceeded by digital instruments, offering much more configurability. Figure 9.9 however, shows a 3 term controller using analogue circuitry. There have been many variations on 3 term control amplifier circuitry (and corresponding algorithms for the digital counter-part). In this example, amplifier U1 is the differential stage, producing an error signal V_e, the difference between the set-point input and feedback voltages. The three terms operate on the error signal,

➡ amplifier U2 produces an output proportional to the error signal, with gain set by R6 and R7;

➡ amplifier U3 is configured as an integrator. If there is an error between set-point and feedback, then Ve will not be zero, so U3 output will ramp at a rate set by R8 and C1;

➡ amplifier U4 is configured as a differentiator, with action time set by C2 and R9.

The outputs of each of the three stages are summed at the input to U5, a unity gain buffer. The output voltage, V_o, can therefore be expressed as

$$V_o = PV_e + I\int V_e + D \cdot \frac{V_e}{dt}$$

Where

$V_e = V_{setpoint} - V_{feedback}$

P is the proportional gain

I is the integral gain

D is the derivative gain

This particular configuration allows each of the three effects to be adjusted by means of the gain control on the output stages of U2, U3 and U4. Adjustment of integral action time (set by R8 and C1) and derivative action time (set by R9 and C2) will also be necessary. In operation, the three terms contribute individually to reduce the error to zero:

➡ the proportional term will produce an output while ever there is an error. Increasing the proportional gain will drive the output higher, the overall effect being to reduce the difference between set-point and feedback;

➡ the integrator will ramp while ever there is an error, the direction of ramp being such that it will operate in anti-phase to the error, ie to reduce the error to zero;

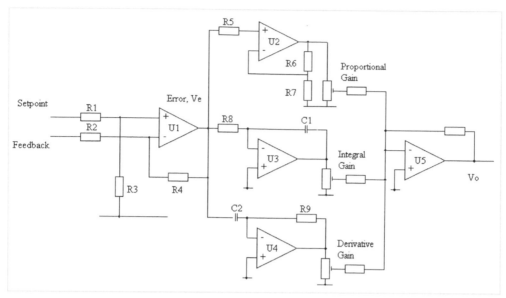

Figure 9.9   *Analogue 3 term controller*

⟹   the differentiator is sensitive to rate-of-change of the error, and will produce an output to counter the effects of rapid change.

Forward path drivers

DC motor drive (linear)

Small dc motors are prevalent in positioning systems, as are hydraulic servo-valves, these typically requiring a 24 volt supply up to a few hundred milli-amps. Figure 9.10 shows a linear output stage with the option to select current setting mode or voltage control mode by means of link Lk1.

TR1 and TR2 operate as emitter followers on the output of the differential amplifier U1, giving the amplifier a much higher current drive capability. Current drawn by the load passes through feedback resistor R_f, producing a feedback voltage proportional to load current.

For motor drives, this has considerable advantage, that the motor can be operated in speed control or torque control:

⟹   with the link selected for voltage feedback, the motor operates in closed loop control with "Armature Voltage Feedback" (AVF). The amplifier controls the output voltage to produce a constant motor speed under varying load conditions (since speed of a dc servomotor is proportional to armature voltage);

➡ with the link selected for current feedback, the motor operates in closed loop control of torque. The amplifier regulates current into the motor (motor torque is proportional to armature current).

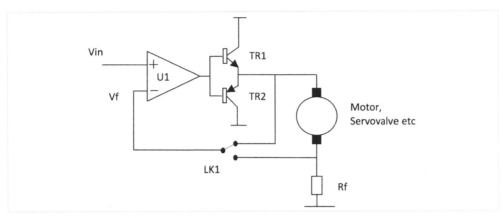

Figure 9.10 Motor drive

For precise speed control applications, the current setting control would be used as an inner loop, with tacho-generator feedback control in an outer loop. AVF mode is effective in speed control, in that it compensated for the output impedance of the drive amplifier, but has a poorer speed control characteristic under load.

For electro-hydraulic system control, the amplifier should be operated in current mode to compensate for varying servo-valve coil temperature.

This circuit is simple and useful for comparatively small output currents, since the output devices require heat sinking for thermal protection.

DC motor drive (switching)

Linear (analogue) motor drives are inefficient due to heat loss in the output stage. A preferred technique is to use a switching driver, such that the output devices are fully on or fully off, thereby reducing their power dissipation. Consider the push-pull output stage comprising TR1 and TR2 in figure 9.10 above. Both transistors operate as current boosters on the output of the amplifier, so they will be passing the full load output current. While conducting, each transistor will have a voltage drop across them between zero and the supply voltage, so device power dissipation will be considerable, hence the requirement for heat sinking and thermal protection.

An alternative technique is to use a "switching" output stage, so that the output devices are either fully on or fully off. In this manner, when the device is fully off, it passes no current so device dissipation is zero, and when the device is fully on, it has a low voltage across it, (ie the saturation voltage of the device), and power dissipation is much reduced.

Switching occurs at high frequency, typically using "Pulse Width Modulation" (PWM), with switching frequencies in the order of 5 kHz to 100 kHz. Figure 9.11 shows how the output is switched between the supply voltage and zero, and the average value is varied by adjustment of the pulse width.

One of the easiest ways to create a PWM waveform is to compare the reference signal with a triangular waveform, as shown in figure 9.12.

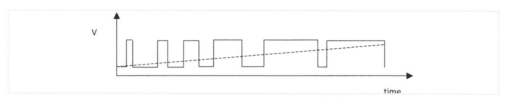

Figure 9.11   *Average value of a PWM waveform*

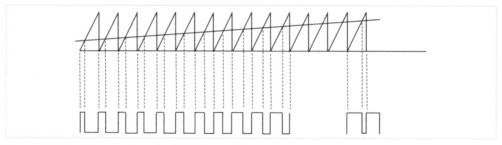

Figure 9.12   *Generation of a PWM waveform*

A suitable circuit is shown in figure 9.13. U1 is configured in a standard arrangement as an astable multi-vibrator, based upon a Schmitt trigger having positive feedback via R2 and R3. C1 charges via R4 towards the output of the amplifier. When the voltage on the capacitor exceeds the feedback voltage set by the resistor ratio R2 and R3, the amplifier output switches to the opposite polarity. The capacitor will then charge in the opposite direction. Hence a regular square wave is generated at the output of the amplifier, switching between the amplifier supply voltages. A capacitor charge waveform is also available from the circuit, which in the example, is used as the ramp to generate the PWM. Frequency is set by R1 and C1. The "ramp" generated by the RC charge / discharge is used as the input waveform to comparator U2. The output of the comparator is either high or low depending upon the relative levels of its two inputs, producing a PWM waveform as shown in figure 9.12. The output signal is used to drive a power device for motor or solenoid control. FETs are preferred as the output device since they have a very low "on" resistance, reducing power loss in the device and resulting in a more efficient drive.

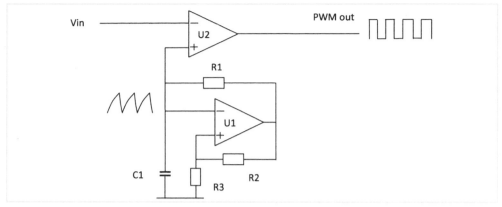

Figure 9.13   PWM generator

Power controller

For heating element control applications (furnaces, ovens etc) the electrical power input to the heater must be regulated. The two most common techniques are "phase angle firing or "burst firing". In phase angle control, the power output device (thyristor or triac) is turned on part way through the mains ac cycle. By variation of the firing angle the average voltage to the load may be regulated. Note that for power control applications (heaters etc), rectification is not necessary. Figure 9.14 shows a phase angle controlled waveform.

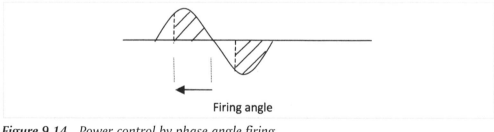

Figure 9.14   Power control by phase angle firing

Figure 9.15   Burst fire power control load waveform

An unfortunate effect of phase angle firing is the high electrical interference caused by switching at peak points in the cycle. The rapid turn-on produces a spike which can be detected not only at the base frequency (ie 50 Hz for the mains supply) but at multiples across the frequency spectrum. For heating applications, it is preferable to control power by allowing a burst of energy for a timed period. Regulation of the timed period produces effective power control, since the average power into the load is controlled. Interference is reduced since the power is applied in complete cycles, switched on at the zero crossing point. Figure 9.15 shows the load waveform.

A burst fired system may be effectively created from a combination of a PWM waveform generator and a zero switching detector. A basic frequency of 2 seconds (100 complete cycles) as a time reference provides full power control in steps of 1%. This type of control is successful in heaters and ovens where thermal inertia is high. Figure 9.16 shows a schematic of how a burst fire waveform could be produced. The PWM signal effectively controls a "gate" allowing the ac power to pass, but the gate is allowed to open only at the zero switching point of the power waveform.

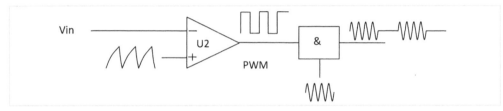

Figure 9.16   Burst fire waveform generation

Summary

This chapter has presented electronic circuit blocks of functions used in signal processing, instrumentation and control. Such analogue circuitry remains commonly used in process plant, and in certain applications will continue to remain analogue. However, some of the functions presented are performed more easily digitally, within an embedded controller.

10
Software Building Blocks

This chapter presents a "sourcebook" of software for some of the most commonly used functions within programmed control systems. Examples are presented in "C" and PIC assembler, including functions used in signal processing for instrumentation as well as in real time control closed loop control and communication.

All code presented has run successfully in industrial control applications, but on a variety of computer hardware. The reader is encouraged to use the code, but to accept that modification will be required depending upon the development environment used and the eventual application.

Moving average (filter)

Digital filters are readily implemented in software, and are generally based upon the algorithm presented in the earlier chapter on instrumentation. Recall the filter algorithm as shown in figure 10.1.

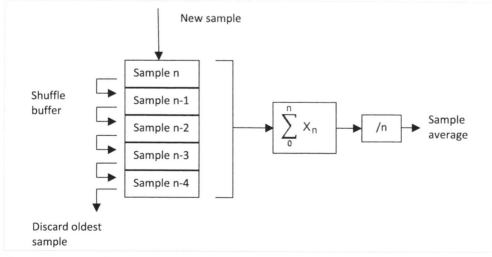

Figure 10.1 *Moving Average Filter Algorithm*

Figure 10.2 presents an example written in C++, taking the average of the last 5 values.

```
for (Sample_Count = 1; 4; Sample_Count++)
  {
     Sample_Table[Count] = Sample_Table[Count+1];
                                   // Shuffle buffer
  }
Sample_Table[5] = New_Value;        // Insert next value

Sample_Sum = 0;
for (Sample_Count = 1; 5; Sample_Count++)
  {
     Sample_Sum = Sample_Sum + Sample_Table[Count];
                               // Sum last readings
  }
Average = Sample_Sum / 5;           // Average
```

Figure 10.2   Moving Average Code

The first block of code shuffles the past samples in the buffer, the oldest sample being lost (by being overwritten). The latest sample is then inserted at the front of the buffer. The average is easily determined by summing the buffer contents and then dividing. A more general routine would use a variable to define the number of samples to be averaged, (ie the filter weight) assuming that a buffer table of suitable length has been defined.

Peak and Trough detection

Detecting the highest value (peak) or lowest value (trough) of a signal is particularly useful for alarm or data capture functions, involving comparison of a current value with another stored value. For peak detection, the higher value is retained, whilst for trough detection, the lower value is retained. Figure 10.3 shows the detection function.

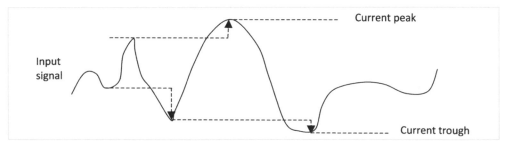

Figure 10.3   Peak and trough detection

Figure 10.4 shows a code segment in C++ to detect the lowest value of a variable called "Tool_Position". For peak and trough detection, a reset function is required, where the detected peak or trough is reset to a start value. This will generally occur at the start of a process cycle and is easily achieved by setting the captured value to the current sample (when the process is presumably in an initial condition before a cycle start). The first part of the code performs the capture, by comparison of the stored lowest value with the current value, updating the stored value if the current value is lower. The second part of the code performs a reset upon a reset request flag being set. The request is cleared after the reset operation.

```
if (Tool_Position < Tool_Lowest_Position)
  {
    Tool_Lowest_Position = Tool_Position;
  }

If (Trough_Reset == 1)
  {
    Tool_Lowest_Position = Tool_Position;
    Trough_Reset = 0;
  }
```

Figure 10.4   Trough detect

Table sort

There are occasions when a table of values is to be sorted into ascending, descending or alphabetical order etc. There are many ways of performing such a sort, similar to the peak detection above, involving comparison of a current value with another stored value. For table sorting, the values are compared and then swapped to place them in order. The most common example is a "bubble sort", so called because the table is scanned and values slowly "drift" their way to the top like bubbles in a liquid. Figure 10.5 presents one such algorithm.

```
Do
  Swap = false
  For i = 1 to length of table
    If table entry[n] < table entry [n+ 1] then
      Swap values
      Swap = true
    Endif
  Next
while swap = false
```

Figure 10.5   Bubble sort algorithm

In operation, a pass is made through the table of values and successive entries compared. If the values are in the wrong order, they are swapped, and a flag set to indicate that a change was made during that pass through the table. This process is repeated until a complete pass is made without a swap being made, indicating that the table elements are in order. The process is slow since the entire table is scanned in a nested loop, up to as many times as the number of elements. The reader is encouraged to review other sources to compare the multitude of such algorithms.

PIC Serial data Transmit / Receive

Software for serial data transmission is particularly interesting since it involves timing issues as well as byte handling and hardware status testing. ASCII code (*American Standard Code for Information Interchange*) is universally used to transmit serial data.

A typical transmit programme would require the instruction sequence

```
if      (Transmitter Ready)
        Read next byte to transmit
        Write byte to transmitter register
End
```

The "Transmitter Ready" signal is a bit test of the transmitter status register, indicating that the last byte has been sent and the transmitter is ready for the next. Normally a string of data forming a message or file would be sent from a table, so a more complete sequence might be

```
Set pointer to start of table
Do until all table sent
    if Transmitter Ready
        Read table for next byte to transmit
        Write byte to transmitter register
    end
Increment table pointer
```

The easiest way to receive characters is to have the receiver interrupt the processor upon character receipt. The character can then be saved in a buffer for later programme use.

Figure 10.6 shows the serial communication section (UART) of the popular PIC family of microcontrollers in a simplified form.

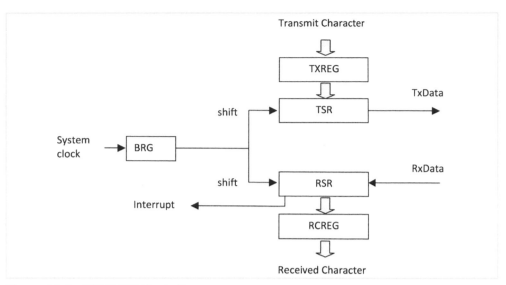

Figure 10.6   PIC UART block diagram

The heart of both transmitter and receiver are the shift registers, TSR and RSR respectively. To transmit, the character in TSR is shifted out at the baud rate. Receive is essentially the opposite process, where the serial data is shifted into RSR, after appropriate level detection and recognition of a valid "Start" bit. Shifting takes place at a rate set by the baud rate generator, BRG. The PIC master clock oscillator is divided by a factor in BRG to produce a frequency corresponding to the desired bit rate. In addition, the Start and Stop bits are added to the outgoing bit stream, and stripped from the incoming stream by additional logic in the UART, to conform to standard serial data transmission protocols.

To transmit and receive data, the UART must first be initialised under programme control to configure baud rate, number of data bits, parity and start/stop bits. Data can then be transmitted by writing to the transmit data register TXREG. Received data is read from the receive data register RCREG either by polling or in an interrupt service routine if "interrupt on character receipt" is enabled.

```
Initialisation
    Program the baud rate generator for the desired
                                    frequency
    Program the data format, number of data bits, parity,
                                    start/stop etc
    Enable interrupt on character receive
Tx/Rx
    Write to the transmitter
    Upon interrupt, read the receiver register
```

Sample transmit subroutine for a PIC series chip

In the example figure 10.7, a 5 character message is transmitted from the buffer TXBUF. There are three sections to the code:

```
TXDATA
;       Transmit buffer
;       Check transmitter status

        banksel   TXSTA
        btfss     TXSTA,TRMT    ;IF transmitter ready
        goto      DONE

;       THEN transmit next character

        banksel   TXBUF
        movlw     TXBUF             ;Index base of buffer
        movwf     FSR
        movf      CHARCNT,W
        addwf     FSR,F           ;Correct for next character
        movf      INDF,W          ;read next digit
        movwf     TXREG   ;and write to transmitter register

        incf      CHARCNT,F       ;Next character
        movlw     0x05
        subwf     CHARCNT,W       ;IF all done
        btfss     STATUS,Z
        goto      DONE
        clrf      CHARCNT      ;THEN reset to first character
DONE
        return
```

Figure 10.7   Transmit routine

➠   upon entry to the routine, the transmitter status is checked by testing the "Transmitter Ready" bit, indicating that any previous character has been shifted out and the transmitter is ready for the next;

➠   the middle section of code reads and ttransmits the next character. The character is read from the buffer by indirect addressing using the variable CHARCNT. A count of the number of characters transmitted is maintained in CHARCNT, which is then used as an offset from the base of the buffer to index the current character. The character is copied from the buffer into the transmit register TXREG;

➠ the final section increments the character count and determines if the message has been completely transmitted (all 5 characters). If the message has not been completed, the next character will be transmitted upon the next programme pass. If all characters of the message have been transmitted, the pointer is reset so that the first message character will be sent at the next transmission.

Sample receive subroutine for a PIC series chip

Figure 10.8 shows a programme sample which polls the receiver to test for a character, checks for framing or overrun errors and saves the character to buffer RXBUF. There are four sections to the code:

➠ upon entry to the routine, the receiver status is checked by testing the "Character Received" bit. If a character is present in the receiver, it is read and saved to a temporary store RXCHR;

➠ the second section of code checks that the received character is valid, by ensuring that no framing or overrun error has occured;

➠ in the third section, the received character is transferred to the next buffer location. The buffer is addressed indirectly using CHRCNT, the received character count, as an offset from the base of the buffer. 10 bytes are transferred, after which the pointer is reset;

➠ the last section is an error handler, which resets the receive logic and flushes the receiver in the event of a receive error.

```
RXDATA
    banksel     PIR1
    btfss       PIR1,RCIF       ;IF character received
    goto        DONE
    movf        RCREG,W         ;then read character
    movwf       RXCHR           ;and save

    btfsc       RCSTA,FERR      ;IF framing error
    goto        RX_ERR
    btfsc       RCSTA,OERR      ;OR overrun error
    goto        RX_ERR          ;THEN ignore character and quit

    movlw       RXBUF           ;ELSE read character and save
    movwf       FSR             ;Index base of receive buffer
```

Figure 10.8   Receive routine

```
        movf        CHRCNT,W
        addwf       FSR,F           ;Index next buffer location
        movf        RXCHR,W         ;get character
        movwf       INDF            ;and save
        incf        CHRCNT,F        ;Increment character count
        movf        CHRCNT,W        ;If 10th received character
        sublw       0x0A
        btfss       STATUS,Z
        goto        DONE
        movlw       0x00
        movwf       CHRCNT          ;THEN reset pointer
RX_ERR
        bcf         RCSTA,CREN      ;Clear any receive errors
        movlw       0x00
        movwf       CHRCNT          ;reset pointer
        bsf         RCSTA,CREN      ;Reset receive logic
        movf        RCREG,W         ;flush buffer
DONE
```

Figure 10.8   Receive routine (cont'd)

PIC analogue input

Figure 10.9 shows the analogue input section of the popular Microchip family of microcontrollers. The operation must be understood before attempting programming, to appreciate the analogue input signal path, channel selection and conversion process.

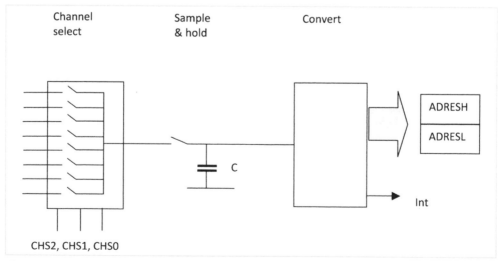

Figure 10.9   Analogue input block diagram

As is common with analogue input systems, the converter is multiplexed (shared) between several input channels. A significant part of the conversion process is to select the desired channel and then allow the input to the converter to settle (ie sample and hold) before starting conversion. The input to the converter is then held at a stable voltage throughout the conversion. The sequence of events in the converter is therefore,

```
Select channel (CHS0, CHS1, CHS2)
Wait for voltage settling time
Start converter

If (conversion complete) then
  Read data
Endif

Repeat
```

The converter must first be initialised under programme control to operate in the desired manner. Analogue inputs can then be acquired as described above. The result is read from two registers ADRESH and ADRESL (high byte and low byte respectively).

```
Initialisation
    Select port as analogue inputs
    Select clock source and frequency
    Enable conversion
    Enable interrupt on conversion complete

Conversion
    Select channel
    Allow to settle
    Start converter
    Read data
```

```
;   SET UP ANALOGUE INPUTS

    banksel    ADCON1
    movlw0x80                    ;All analogue inputs, high byte
                                 ;right justified
    movwf      ADCON1
```

Figure 10.10 *Analogue to digital converter initialisation*

```
        banksel   ADCON0
        movlw     0x81          ;clock at f/32, enable A/D,
                                ;Channel 0
        movwf     ADCON0
```

Figure 10.10   Analogue to digital converter initialisation (cont'd)

Figure 10.10 shows sample code for initialisation. The section INIT runs once on power up, setting the output data format, internal clock source and enabling the converter.

The section ANALIN runs constantly, performing channel selection, conversion start and data read. Note that the code is implemented in "state" form:

State	Process	Exit condition
Read	Read converter result	Data taken
Wait	End-of conversion time delay	Timeout
Channel select	Set CHS0, CHS1, CHS2 for channel	Select complete
Acquire channel	Acquisition time delay	Timeout
Start conversion	Start converter	Start completed

Figure 10.11 shows the sample code for converter control. The current state is set in the variable MODE, which can assume values of 0, 1, 2, 3 or 4, corresponding to the five states described above.

The first part of the code determines the current state and jumps to the appropriate section. At the end of each section the next state is set, so that on the next pass, the correct code for the current state is executed.

The timers are implemented by simple programme loop decrement. The time is set by writing a value into the timer variable, which is decremented upon each programme pass. When the timer has counted down to zero, the time has expired and the next state set.

It is not usually good practice to implement timers in this manner, since the code segment may not be implemented at regular intervals (depending on which other tasks the processor is performing) so the timed period may be variable. If the code segment is called at fixed time intervals under operating system timer control, then the method is simple and effective.

An interesting programming technique is implemented in the "Select Channel" section, using a coded look-up table to determine the bit pattern for the selected channel to be OR'ed into the setup byte.

```
;           Reads A-D converter continuously
;           Stores results in AD0-AD7
;
            EXTERN    AD_MODE, CHANNEL, AD0, ADTIME, DIGIN
;
READ        EQU0
WAIT        EQU1
SELECT      EQU2
ACQUIRE     EQU3
START       EQU4
;
                      CODE
            GLOBAL    ANALIN


ANALIN
;           Determine current A-D programme state and go to
;           appropriate code section

            movlw     READ
            subwf     AD_MODE,w        ;Read data
            btfsc     STATUS,Z
            goto      READ_AD

            movlw     WAIT
            subwf     AD_MODE,w        ;Wait before
                                       ;next conversion
            btfsc     STATUS,Z
            goto      END_WAIT

            movlw     SELECT
            subwf     AD_MODE,w;Select next channel
            btfsc     STATUS,Z
            goto      SELECT_CHANNEL

            movlw     ACQUIRE
            subwf     AD_MODE,w        ;Acquire channel
            btfsc     STATUS,Z
            goto      ACQUIRE_CHANNEL

            movlw     START
            subwf     AD_MODE,w        ;Start converter
            btfsc     STATUS,Z
```

Figure 10.11 *Analogue to Digital converter control*

```
            goto      CONVERT
    ;
    ;
    ;         Read converted data
    READ_AD
            btfsc     ADCONO,NOT_DONE   ;IF conversion
                                        ;complete
            goto      DONE
            movlw     AD0               ;Index base of results
                                        ;table
            movwf     FSR

            bcf       STATUS,C
            rlf       CHANNEL,W         ;Get current channel *
                                        ;2 as table index
            addwf     FSR,F             ;Correct index for
                                        ;channel number

            movf      ADRESH,W          ;Read high byte
            movwf     INDF              ;and save
            incf      FSR,F
            movf      ADRESL,W          ;Read low byte
            movwf     INDF              ;and save

            movlw     WAIT              ;Set wait mode
            movwf     AD_MODE
            movlw     0x02              ;Set end-of-convert-
                                        ;wait (min. 4us)
            movwf     ADTIME
            goto      DONE
    :
    ;         Wait before next acquisition
    ;
    END_WAIT
            decfsz    ADTIME,F          ;IF timer expired
            goto      DONE

            movlw     SELECT            ;THEN set select mode
            movwf     AD_MODE
            goto      DONE
    :
    :
```

Figure 10.11 *Analogue to Digital converter control (cont'd)*

```
;          Select next channel
;
SELECT_CHANNEL
          incf        CHANNEL,F          ;Next channel

          movlw       0x08
          subwf       CHANNEL,W          ;IF all done
          btfsc       STATUS,Z
          clrf        CHANNEL            ;THEN reset to
                                         ;channel 0

          movlw       HIGH SET_CHANNEL
          movwf       PCLATH
          movf        CHANNEL,W          ;Get channel number
          call        SET_CHANNEL        ;Adjust for ADCON0
          iorlw       0x81               ;Set up ADCON0, f/32,
                                         ;channel, enable
          movwf       ADCON0

          movlw       ACQUIRE            ;Set acquire mode
          movwf       AD_MODE
          movlw       0x05               ;Set voltage settling
                                         ;time (min. 20us)
          movwf       ADTIME
          goto        DONE
:
;          Voltage settling time
:
ACQUIRE_CHANNEL
          decfsz      ADTIME,F           ;IF timer expired
          goto        DONE

          movlw       START              ;THEN set start mode
          movwf       AD_MODE
          goto        DONE
;
;
;          Start converter
CONVERT
          bsf         ADCON0,GO          ;Start converter
          movlw       READ               ;Set read mode
          movwf       AD_MODE
```

Figure 10.11   *Analogue to Digital converter control (cont'd)*

```
;
DONE
        return
:
:
;        Lookup bit data for ADCON0 for selected channel
SET_CHANNEL
            addwf   PCL,F              ;Lookup
            retlw   0x00               ;Channel 0
            retlw   0x08               ;Channel 1
            retlw   0x10
            retlw   0x18
            retlw   0x20
            retlw   0x28
            retlw   0x30
            retlw   0x38               ;Channel 7
            End
```

Figure 10.11   *Analogue to Digital converter control (cont'd)*

Real time operating system

For real time control software, a supervisory operating system is required to run tasks at timed intervals. Different processors (PIC, PC, PLC, PAC etc) implement this in different ways and much depends upon the control system architecture, type of process, software tasks and response required.

For complex plant systems, a PLC or PAC would be the processor of choice. PLCs offer task control by execution of selected ladder segments at selected time intervals (eg 10 msec, 50 msec, 1 sec etc). Similarly, PACs have the ability to perform programme control at timed intervals and to schedule operator functions with appropriate priorities.

In PC systems, high level languages offer timing functions, but execution depends very much on the PC operating system, especially where graphic content is high and other tasks are running. In this case it is useful to retain the PC for HMI functions only, and to use real time capabilities of plug-in cards where available to ensure deterministic operation. Whilst PC operating systems are becoming increasingly complex, with multitasking and multithreading capability, it must be remembered that desktop applications are graphic and highly processor intensive and the PC may not be the most suitable control platform.

For embedded systems, it is relatively straightforward to produce a highly reliable operating system based on simple "Foreground / background" techniques using interrupts. Recall the section in an earlier chapter describing interrupts as shown again in figure 10.12

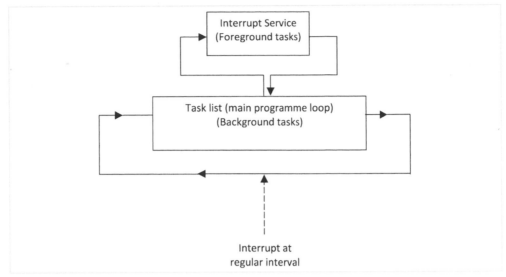

Figure 10.12   Interrupt mechanism

The processor clock is divided to generate an interrupt at 1 millisecond or 10 milli-second intervals. The interrupt service routine is used to call subroutines which require regular execution, whilst non-time-critical tasks are left in the main back-ground loop to run in a "round robin" fashion. The interrupt service routine can divide the interrupt interval further to call tasks at longer time intervals.

In this manner, the processor seemingly multitasks, by running different tasks at different intervals. The real time aspect is guaranteed by placing tasks in fore-ground. For machine or plant control operations, the HMI, keyboard, display and data transmission functions can be run in the background, while process or motion control, interlocking and safety tasks can be run in the foreground.

A programme for a PIC microcontroller is presented here to perform real time con-trol, with time critical tasks on the regular interrupt and other tasks in the back-ground. There are several parts to the code and each is described in the following text.

Figure 10.13 shows how the interrupt service routine (ISR) is configured. In this particular processor, the address of the ISR is stored in a dedicated area of the pro-cessor programme memory. The section INT_VECTOR writes the programme ad-dress of the ISR into the interrupt vector address, so that upon receipt of an interrupt, the processor can read the ISR address and execute accordingly. The code is placed at absolute memory address 0004. When an interrupt occurs, execution continues from that address. Note that the current context (accumulator and status register) is saved, before the main ISR (INTSRV) is called. When INTSRV has completed execution, the saved context is restored before issuing a return from interrupt command to resume processing from where it left off when the interrupt occurred.

Figure 10.14 shows the main programme loop. At power up, having performed the ISR setup as above, the processor continues execution at the label START. The initialisation task is called, followed by all the background tasks in sequence. When

```
;
INT_VECTOR          CODE    0x004       ;Interrupt vector
;
        movwf       W_SAVE              ;Save context
        movf        STATUS,W
        movwf       S_SAVE

        call        INTSRV              ;Service interrupt

        movf        S_SAVE,W
        movwf       STATUS
        movf        W_SAVE,W
;
        retfie      ;Return from interrupt
```

Figure 10.13   ISR vector setting

```
        CODE
;
START
        call        INIT                ;Set up ports

LOOP
;
        call        KEYS                ;Operator keyboard
        call        SCALE               ;Scale analogue values
        call        CAPTURE             ;Capture data
        call        DISPLAY             ;Operator display
        call        TXPC                ;Transmit data
        goto        LOOP

End
```

Figure 10.14   Main programme background loop

the last task has completed, the programme loops back to run all the background tasks again. Note that INIT is run only once for initialisation purposes.

The initialisation programme sets up the ports and performs other once-only power up tasks. Figure 10.15 shows how the initialisation routine INIT, where a timer is configured to accept the processor clock as an input and use the divided output as a processor interrupt.

```
INIT
;
;          SET UP TIMER 1 FOR INTERRUPT SOURCE
           movlw      0x31            ; 8:1 prescale,
                                      ;oscillator off,
                                      ;internal clock,
                                      ;enable
           movwf      T1CON
;
;          SET UP PERIPHERAL INTERRUPTS
           movlw      0x01
           movwf      PIE1            ;Interrupt mask

           bcf        PIR1,TMR1IF     ;Clear any timer 1
                                      ;interrupt
           bsf        PIE1, TMR1IE    ;Enable timer 1
                                      ;interrupt

           bsf        INTCON,PEIE     ;Enable peripheral
                                      ;interrupts
           bsf        INTCON,GIE      ;Global interrupt
                                      ;enable
;
           return
           End
```

Figure 10.15   *Initialisation – Interrupt clock configuration*

In this example, Timer1 is used to divide the processor clock by 8, and then the processor interrupt from Timer1 enabled.

Figure 10.16 shows the interrupt service routine INTSRV, which calls all the foreground tasks and then resets Timer1 to its start value. The clock frequency fed into the timer is actually one quarter of the processor clock, so to obtain an interrupt every 1 millisecond based upon a crystal oscillator frequency of 20MHz, the divider can be calculated:

$$n = \frac{20 \text{ MHz}}{4 \cdot 8 \cdot 1000}$$

A value of 625 (FD8F$_{16}$) is written to the timer.

```
INTSRV
;
;            1mSec tasks
;
             call      TIMERS        ;Process timing
             call      ANALIN        ;Analogue inputs
             call      DIGIN         ;Digital inputs
             call      MACHINE       ;machine control
             call      OUTPUTS       ;Outputs
;
;
;            Reset interrupt timer
;
             movlw     0xfd          ;Preset timer for 625
                                     ;(20MHz xtal,
                                     ;/8 prescaler)
             movwf     TMR1H
             movlw     0x8f
             movwf     TMR1L
             bcf       PIR1,TMR1IF   ;Clear timer 1 interrupt
             bsf       T1CON,TMR1ON  ;Restart timer
;
DONE
             return
             End
```

Figure 10.16   ISR foreground tasks

3 term (PID) control

There are several algorithms for 3 term control and many control engineers will at some point consider writing such a piece of code. Figure 10.17 shows an example in "C++" made up of four sections:

➡   the first part of the programme determines the process error, as the difference between set-point and the process variable (measured value);

➡   the second section determines a rate of change by subtraction of the current measured value from the measured value "last time round". A timer is used to ensure that a reliable, consistent time base for the rate of change is achieved. The current measured value is then saved to become the "last time round" value on the next pass;

➠ the third section integrates the error as a simple first order lag. A fraction of the error is added to the integrator output at timed intervals, ensuring that the output will ramp up or down correctly based upon error polarity;

➠ the final section sums the three terms.

The code is self-explanatory in function.

```
// DETERMINE ERROR
Error = Setpoint - Measured_Value;

// DERIVATIVE ELEMENT
// Calculate rate of change of Derivative control
if (HasDownTimerExpired(Change_Rate_Timer))
  {
  Change_Rate_Timer = Change_Rate_Time;
  Change_Rate = Measured_Value - Measured_Value_Old;
  Measured_Value_Old = Measured_Value;
}

// INTEGRAL ELEMENT
// Integrate error
if (HasDownTimerExpired(Error_Summation_Timer))
  {
  Error_Summation_Timer = Error_Summation_Time;
  // Determine a suitable fraction of the error value to
  //add to the integrator output
  Error_Fraction = Error / Error_Divisor;
  Error_Integrator = Error_Integrator + Error_Fraction;
  }

// 3 TERM CONTROLLER (PID summation)
Proportional_Term = (Error * Proportional_Gain);
Derivative_Term = (Change_Rate * Derivative_Gain);
Integral_Term = (Error_Integrator * Integral_Gain);

PID_Output = Proportional_Term + Derivative_Term +
             Integral_Term;
```

Figure 10.17 *3-Term Controller*

In practice, whilst the generation of the three components is relatively easy, the implementation to a practical system is not so straightforward, since

➠ the derivative term should determine the rate of change over a suitable time period, the time depending upon process reaction and variable change time. Too short a time period introduces noise, too long a time period causes instability;

➠ similarly, the integrator sums error occurring over a timed period. Too short a time period makes any change ineffective, and too long to correct for errors, too long a period introduces large correction factors and instability.

A general rule of thumb, and hence a starting point for tuning the controller, would be to set the derivative and integral time periods to one-tenth the process time constant, such that the controller can update the output signal 10 times during the fast change portion of the time response, and will continue to contribute to the output for 40 further periods before the output settles (ie for a 5 time constant period).

The contribution of each term (ie its effectiveness) can be varied by increasing the individual gains in the summation part of the programme.

A recommended set-up procedure would be:

> Determine the process time constant
> Set the derivative and integral timers
> Start with Derivative and Integral gains at zero
> Increase Proportional gain and observe the process output response
> Increase proportional gain until the onset of output overshoot
> If error is present, slowly introduce integral control by increasing the Integral gain
> If overshoot is significant, reduce Proportional gain
> Increase the Derivative gain to dampen oscillation

Summary

This chapter has presented code samples in C and in PIC assembly language for common control engineering programming requirements. The programmes are intended for illustrative purposes only, and are not presented as examples of programming excellence, but may be used to form part of more complete projects as required.

11
Putting it all together – a control example

This chapter draws upon all the material and ideas developed in previous chapters to build a complete control system. The system is to be controlled by software in closed loop, so we shall develop the hardware and software requirements.

The example takes the following steps:

⮕ the system;

⮕ control requirements;

⮕ I/O;

⮕ programming;

⮕ tuning.

The system

Consider the common application of speed control of a dc servomotor. The motor has an applied voltage V_a, armature resistance R_a, and drives an inertial and frictional load, with output speed ω. The motor model is developed in Chapter 2 based upon system components shown again in figure 11.1.

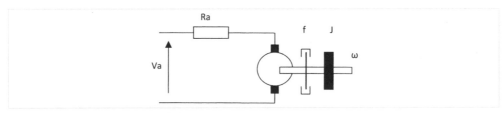

Figure 11.1 *The motor model*

From chapter 2, we have the system transfer function

$$\omega(s) = V(s) \cdot \frac{K}{1 + sT}$$

where

$$K = \frac{K_t}{f R_a + K_\omega K_t}$$

and

$$T = \frac{J R_a}{f R_a + K_\omega K_t}$$

Using the same motor parameters, for the motor we have

$$\omega(s) = V(s) \cdot \frac{0.5}{1 + s \cdot 0.22}$$

Control requirements

For the typical speed control application, we require the motor to maintain constant speed under applied load. If we were to use the motor alone (open loop), then as the load increased, armature current would increase, therefore the voltage "lost" across the armature resistance would increase and the motor speed would reduce. This load/speed characteristic is shown in figure 11.2.

The control requirement is to operate in closed loop to maintain speed over the full load range of the motor (ie to maximum rated armature current).

The loop is closed by a tacho-generator providing speed feedback, so under increasing load conditions, the fall in speed produces an increase in error and hence

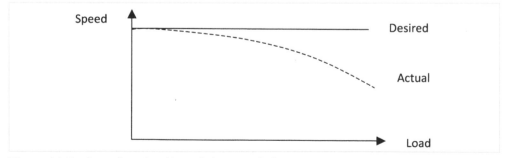

Figure 11.2   Open loop load/speed characteristic

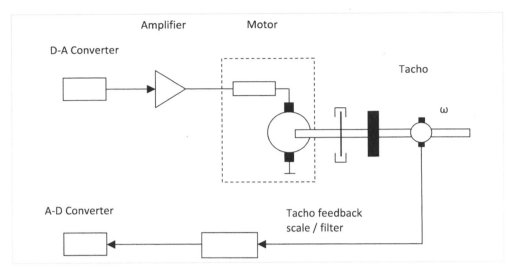

Figure 11.3   Closed loop motor speed control

an increased drive voltage to the motor enabling it to meet the load demand. Figure 11.3 shows the complete system. Note the inclusion of interface hardware, and the power amplifier.

The error determination will be performed in software, along with any required gain and tuning requirements. The closed loop system and its analysis is essentially the same as in the previous work presented on modelling, transient response etc., but note that we have now introduced two additional factors:

➠   the computer programme, which will have a scan rate;

➠   the resolution of the analogue to digital and the digital to analogue converters.

we also have the practical limitations of the drive hardware (current limit). Earlier, we considered real time programming and interfacing issues.

So far we have analysed systems in the time and frequency domains, and have represented them in the Laplace domain for convenience. In the same way that the Laplace transform is used as a tool to analyse continuous-time systems, the "z transform" is used for analysis of "sampled data" systems. For the purposes of this example, we shall continue to operate in the time domain and use simulation techniques previously considered.

I/O

For the purpose of this example, we shall use a high level language and assume the availability of suitable hardware, but consider the interfacing requirements.

> **Aside – z Transforms**
>
> The z transform technique is as important in the analysis of digital systems as the Laplace transform is in continuous systems. There is a mathematical basis for the transform but it is beyond the scope of this introductory text. The reader is encouraged to view alternative reference. The technique provides a simple, convenient method for solution of sampled data systems using standard types and table look-up, in a similar manner to which the Laplace transform provides solutions for continuous systems.

For the analogue output, our programme will produce an amplified error value (in units of rev/sec or radian/sec). This value will be converted into an analogue signal to pass to the motor drive amplifier. It is necessary to consider the practical implications and the scaling of this signal.

For a typical industrial grade analogue-to digital converter, we have 13 bit resolution (12 data bits plus a sign bit) producing –10 to +10 volts. The amplified error signal must therefore be within the range –4095 to +4095. The speed of the motor can be controlled to one part in 4096 (0.02%) which will be quite adequate for a practical system.

For the analogue input, the programme will receive a speed feedback signal, which can be scaled for readout display (in units of rev/sec or rad/sec). Again, with typical industrial grade hardware, a 12 bit result will be produced. There will inevitably be some level shifting and filtering required for the tacho-generator, since a standard output device would produce 60 volts / 1000 rpm (ie 0 – 90 volts for a typical 0 – 1500 rpm speed control system).

Tacho-generators are inherently noisy since it has armature and brushes. (A pulse counting system would produce a more convenient voltage level, but would require similar filtering). The level shift and filter therefore introduces a gain and phase consideration as we have already seen.

The drive amplifier should be capable of producing the motor rated current at full power. Note that the output voltage swing should exceed the motor rated voltage in order that sufficient drive can be produced at full power output (to give sufficient control overhead at full torque, full speed). Using the same motor parameters as in the example of chapter 2, our amplifier requires an output in excess of 24 volts, with a current rating in the order of 20 Amps.

From our earlier work on motor drives, we would choose a switched drive, with FET or thyristor output stage. Note that in this case, the voltage gain is relatively low at a value of 2.4, (nominally10 volts in produces 24 volts out) but the power gain is high given the output power of 480 Watts (24 volts at 20 Amps).

Programming

The control programme has several requirements:

⮕   operator entry of demanded speed;

⮕   display of actual speed;

⮕   determination of error, followed by PID control.

If the system were a small embedded application, we would choose a PIC device to implement the control strategy, and provide operator entry/display via a small LCD display. A PIC could also provide diagnostics, serial setting of demand and feedback etc. A simple foreground/background operating system would be ideal in this case.

As part of a larger plant control system, we might choose a PAC, using an internal PID loop to control the motor. A SCADA system might then be used for speed setting, feedback and diagnostics.

For our example, we shall simulate the system in the high level language C# using Euler integration techniques. This will also facilitate the inclusion of a three term control strategy in the same programme, in order that the effects of tuning may be visualised.

The motor is presented for Euler integration as shown in figure 11.4, incorporating the motor parameters above and an amplifier voltage gain of 2.4 as described.

Figures 11.5 and 11.6 are a listing of code in C# for the motor speed control simulation, incorporating 3 term closed loop control. The reader is encouraged to repeat and prove by experimentation, and to vary parameters to observe the effects. As in previous simulation examples, the simulation is calculated at each time interval for a fixed time period. The output variable is simply written to a text box, but could equally be written to an array or saved to disc for later graphing.

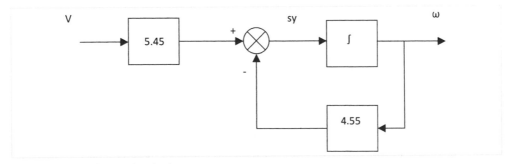

Figure 11.4   *Motor simulation*

For the motor parameters given, a suitable time step for calculation is 0.1 second, running for a 1 second period.

The programme is slightly different to previous code examples in that it is presented in C# for use on a PC, and therefore includes attendant code for the form interface. It has four distinct sections, which are easily identified in the listing:

⟹   variable declarations;

⟹   error determination from desired speed and simulated motor speed;

⟹   three term controller, which determines the error and produces an output to the drive;

⟹   motor and drive simulation.

Since this is a simulation, it runs in "simulated time" (ie at the speed the PC runs the C# programme, but each loop is one simulation time step). Integral and derivative actions are calculated at each time step based upon the error calculation in that particular scan.

```csharp
using System;
using System.Collections.Generic;
using System.ComponentModel;
using System.Data;
using System.Drawing;
using System.Linq;
using System.Text;
using System.Windows.Forms;


namespace Motor_Speed_Control
{
  public partial class Form1 : Form
  {
    public double Desired_Speed = 10;    // Operator input
                                         // desired speed
    public double Actual_Speed;          // System output,
                                         // motor actual speed
    public double Speed_Error;
    public double Controller_Output;  // Controller output
                                      // (and speed demand
                                      // to drive)
```

Figure 11.5   *Variable declarations for the motor speed control simulation*

```
      public double Proportional_Term;   // 3 term controller
                                         // components
      public double Integral_Term;
      public double Derivative_Term;
      public double Speed_Error_Old;
      public double Error_Integrator;

      public double P;                    // Proportional gain
      public double I;                    // Integral gain
      public double D;                    // Derivative gain

      public double dt = 0.1;             // Time interval
      public double time_elapsed;         // Total time
      public double period = 2;           // Simulation period

      public double sw;                   // Integrator input
      public double K = 5.45;
      public double T = 4.55;
```

Figure 11.5   *Variable declarations for the motor speed control simulation (cont'd)*

```
  public Form1()
    {
      InitializeComponent();
    }

  private void Form1_Load(object sender, EventArgs e)
    {
    }

  private void button1_Click(object sender, EventArgs e)
    {
      // Run simulation
      while (time_elapsed < period)
      {
        // Determine error
        Speed_Error = Desired_Speed - Actual_Speed;

        //Controller
        Proportional_Term = Speed_Error * P;
        Integral_Term = (Error_Integrator +
                    (Error_Integrator + Speed_Error) * I);
```

Figure 11.6   *Motor speed control simulation code (C#)*

```
      Derivative_Term = (Speed_Error_Old - Speed_Error)*D;
      Speed_Error_Old = Speed_Error;
      Controller_Output = Proportional_Term +
                          Integral_Term + Derivative_Term;

      // Motor Euler simulation
      sw = (Controller_Output * 5.45) -
          (Actual_Speed / 4.55);
      Actual_Speed = (sw * dt) + Actual_Speed;
      listBox1.Items.Add(time_elapsed + " " +
          Actual_Speed);
      time_elapsed = time_elapsed + dt;

  }
}

private void textBox1_TextChanged(object sender,
                                  EventArgs e)
{
  Desired_Speed = double.Parse(textBox1.Text);
}
private void textBox7_TextChanged(object sender,
                                  EventArgs e)
{
  period = double.Parse(textBox7.Text);
}
private void textBox8_TextChanged(object sender,
                                  EventArgs e)
{
  dt = double.Parse(textBox8.Text);
}
private void textBox4_TextChanged(object sender,
                                  EventArgs e)
{
  P = double.Parse(textBox4.Text);
}
private void textBox5_TextChanged(object sender,
                                  EventArgs e)
{
  I = double.Parse(textBox5.Text);
}
private void textBox6_TextChanged(object sender,
```

Figure 11.6   *Motor speed control simulation code (C#) (cont'd)*

```
                                      EventArgs e)
    {
       D = double.Parse(textBox6.Text);
    }
  }
}
```

Figure 11.6   Motor speed control simulation code (C#) (cont'd)

Figure 11.7 shows the operator interface screen for the simulation.

Figure 11.7   Simulation programme display screen

Tuning

Using the simulation programme, it is easy to change values, run the simulation again and observe the effects. In this manner, the optimum values for P, I and D can be determined, in the same way a real system would be tuned.

For our purposes, it is sufficient to see the effects of the integral and derivative terms upon the output, and record the differences. Figure 11.8 is a table showing the steps taken in the tuning process.

Desired speed	P	I	D	Final value	Comment
10	1	0	0	9.61	Typical 1st order response
10	1	1	0	9.8	Improved final value
10	1	2	0	9.87	Onset of oscillation
10	1	2	0.5	9.87	Ideal

Figure 11.8   System tuning

Initially, the proportional term only is used and the response observed. The forward path gain is sufficient to produce a steady state error of only 3.9%. The integral term is added and increased to reduce the error, but introduces oscillation on the output. The derivative term acts to reduce oscillations and produces an ideal time response.

Summary

This chapter has incorporated elements of all previous chapters in the simulation of a complete motor speed control system. Having considered modelling and interface requirements, a simulation programme has been produced in C#. The simulation incorporated three term control and provided a useful tool to examine the effects of the three terms upon the controlled variable.

The reader is encouraged to repeat and experiment with the programme.

12
Further Reading

The individual chapters in this book have focussed on a particular aspect of control engineering or supporting technologies. Each chapter represents a complete subject area its own right and it would not be possible to completely explore each in any depth within the scope of the text.

It is hoped that there is sufficient material for the reader to gain an appreciation of control engineering methodologies. The following presents sources of text and web information.

Texts

Ken Dutton, Steve Thompson, Bill Barraclough,
The Art of Control Engineering; ISBN-10: 0201175452

Norman S Nise,
Control Systems Engineering; ISBN-10: 0470169974

Richard C Dorf,
Modern Control Systems; ISBN-10: 0132451921

B E Jones,
Instrumentation, Measurement and Feedback; ISBN-10: 0070993831

Paul Horowitz, Winfield Hill,
The Art of Electronics; ISBN-10: 0521370957

A S Sedra, K C Smith,
Microelectronic Circuits; ISBN-10: 0195142527

John Allwork,
C# 2008 And .NET Programming for Electronic Engineers;
ISBN 978-0-905705-81-1

John Allwork,
Visual Studio C# 2010 Programming and PC Interfacing;
ISBN 978-0-905705-95-8

Glyn James,
Modern Engineering Mathematics; ISBN 0-13-018319-9

Useful Web resources

http://www.automation.com/

http://wikis.controltheorypro.com/index.php?title=Main_Page

http://www.mathworks.co.uk/

http://www.ni.com/labview/

http://www.modbus.org/

http://www.opcfoundation.org/

http://www.microchip.com

Web search keywords

The following keywords are suggested for use in an internet search engine, from which many results will be produced. Some discretion is required to identify useful material appropriate to the area of study. Results of a search will inevitably produce material which is highly relevant, but will also produce material to be ignored. Keywords below are grouped into the topic areas of the supporting chapters.

Feedback control, Closed loop, Frequency response, Transient response, Root locus, Classical control, Linear systems, PID, 3 term control, control system stability, automation theory, final value theorem, bandwidth

Numerical simulation, numerical methods, Euler integration, Runge-Kutta, Matlab, Simulink, Mathcad, analogue computer, finite elements

PLC, PAC, OPC, DDE, SCADA, Modbus, Modbus/TCP, RTU, Cyclic Redundancy Check

SSI interface, Profibus, Fieldbus, Devicenet

Statistical process control, key process indicators

Analogue to digital converter, anti-alias filter, digital to analogue converter, microprocessor interfacing, optical isolation

Signal processing hardware, instrumentation amplifier, loop powered transmitters, signal converters, electronic filter, digital filter

Motor speed control, dc drive, servo amplifier, power control, zero voltage switching, zero crossing detector, thyristor, triac, burst firing

Real time programming, C, PIC, assembly language, embedded software, embedded control

Bubble sort, peak detection algorithm

Z transforms, sampled data systems

13
Conclusions

In this book we have touched on several aspects of control engineering, including:

⟹   system description and modelling;

⟹   time and frequency response;

⟹   stability and tuning;

⟹   simulation;

⟹   electronic hardware for instrumentation and control;

⟹   instrumentation and SCADA;

⟹   data communication, hardware, software and protocols;

⟹   software for real time control.

Subject matter is drawn from different but allied disciplines, the diversity of the material illustrating the range of skills required by the modern control engineer.

In a text of this nature, it has not been possible to treat each area with rigour, but as a whole, the text does present a broad-based introduction to control engineering.

The purpose of the book is to whet the appetite and provide background for students, as well as providing sufficient material and theory for practicing engineers requiring deeper knowledge.

It is hoped that the academic content has been deep enough to give an understanding of the necessary analytical techniques, whilst the practical content has been sufficient to develop confidence in design, experimentation and delivery of industrial control systems.

Index